BASIC KNOWLEDGE 'S' GRADE MATHEMATICS
(Revised Edition)

J.F. MORGAN

© J.F. Morgan, 1990.

ISBN 0 7169 3150 8

ROBERT GIBSON · Publisher
17 Fitzroy Place, Glasgow, G3 7SF.

INTRODUCTION

Basic Knowledge Standard Grade Mathematics is intended to serve as a notebook and homework guide for students preparing for the Standard Grade Examination in Mathematics.

The detailed Contents pages will show that the work covers the essential subject matter to meet the requirements of the course at all levels with more than 100 examples and 150 diagrams set in clear, simple text.

CONTENTS

Length, Area, Weight, Volume and Capacity, Temperature, Time 6
Factors and H.C.Fs 9
Prime Factors 9
Common Factors 10
Fractions 11
Multiplication of Fractions 11
Equal Fractions 11
Division of Fractions 13
Improper (Top Heavy) Fractions 13
Percentages and Fractions 14
Changing Fractions to Decimals 14
Changing Decimals to Percentages 15
Multiples and L.C.Ms. 15
Powers and Indices 16
Ordered Fractions 17
Simple Interest 18
Compound Interest 18
Standard Form or Scientific Notation 19
Rounding off, and Significant Figures 20
Average Speed, Time and Distance 22
Addition and Subtraction with Fractions 24
Perimeters 27
Areas and Volumes 28
Square Roots 34
Accounts for Electricity or Gas 37
Profit and Loss 38
Percentage Profit and Loss 39
Hire Purchase and Discount 40
Ratios and Scales 40
Scale Models 42
Direct and Inverse Proportion 43
Foreign Exchange 44
House Purchase 45
Insurance 46
Income Tax 47
Number Bases 48
Error and Tolerance 51
Probability and Arrangements 53
Grouped Frequency Distribution Tables 61
Pie Chart 62
Bar Graph 64
Line Graph 65
Sequences, n^{th} Terms 66
Flow Charts 70
Index Numbers 72
An Investigation 73

3

POINTS 75

LINES 75
  Parallel Lines 75
  Horizontal Lines 75
  Vertical Lines 76
  Perpendicular Lines 76
  Bisecting Lines 77

ANGLES 77
  Acute Angles 77
  Right Angles 78
  Obtuse Angles 78
  Supplementary Angles 80
  Complementary Angles 80
  Compass Bearings 80
  Three-figure Bearings 81

PLANE FIGURES 82
  Triangles 82
  The Square 83
  The Rectangle 84
  The Circle 1 85

SOLID SHAPES OR 3D SHAPES 86
  The Cube 86
  The Cuboid 87
  The Pyramid 87
  The Cone 88
  The Cylinder 88
  The Sphere 89

DRAWING PARALLEL LINES 90

DRAWING TRIANGLES 91

NETS OF SOLIDS 94
  Net of a Cube 94
  Net of a Cuboid 94
  Net of a Square Pyramid 95

PERIMETER 95
  Circumference of a Circle 96

AREA 97
  Area of a Square 97
  Area of a Rectangle 97
  Area of a Right-angled Triangle 97
  Area of a Circle 98

VOLUME 99
  Volume of a Cube 99
  Volume of a Cuboid 99

LINE SYMMETRY 100
  $\frac{1}{2}$-Turn and $\frac{1}{4}$-Turn Symmetry 102

RATIO 102
  Congruent Figures 103
  Similar Figures 103
  Enlargement and Reduction 104
  Drawing Enlargements 104
SINE, COSINE AND TANGENT 106
NEGATIVE NUMBERS AND THE NUMBER LINE 106
  Square Numbers 107
  Triangular Numbers 108
PYTHAGORAS' THEOREM 108
RELATED ANGLES 109
  Corresponding Angles 109
  Alternate Angles 109
  Vertically Opposite Angles 109
  Allied Angles 109
  Angles of Elevation and Depression 110
COORDINATES 110
  Equation of a Straight Line 1 111
ALTITUDES OF A TRIANGLE 112
  Medians of a Triangle 112
THE CIRCLE 2 113
  Length of arc 115
  Area of sector 115
  Equation of circle 116
SINE, COSINE AND TANGENT OF 30°, 45° and 60° 117
  Graphs of sin $x°$, cos $x°$ and tan $x°$ 118
  Polar Coordinates 120
  Distance Formula 121
  Mid-point of a Line Segment 121
  The Area of a Triangle (Trig.) 121
  The Sine Rule 122
  The Cosine Rule 122
VARIATION 123
INDICES 123
CHANGING THE SUBJECT OF A FORMULA 124
EQUATION OF A STRAIGHT LINE 2 124
  Systems of Equations 126
  Inequations (Linear) 127
EXPANDING BRACKETS 128
FACTORISING 128
QUADRATIC EQUATIONS 129
  The Parabola (Graph of a Quadratic Function) 130
  Quadratic Inequations 133
LOCUS 134
SURDS 135
ALGEBRAIC FRACTIONS 135
ACCURATE DRAWINGS 140
FORMULÆ 143

LENGTH

The metre (m) is used to measure dress or curtain material, the length of carpet for the living room or a person's height, e.g. a guardsman or a basketball player will be about 2 m tall.

The metre is a little more than a yard (yd).

The centimetre (cm) is used to measure the size of a suit or jumper or jeans, e.g. the chest size for a slim person is about 94 cm and waist size about 76 cm. The centimetre replaces the inch (1 inch $= 2\frac{1}{2}$ cm). The measurements given above would be chest 37 inches, waist 30 inches.

100 cm $= 1$ m, i.e. a centimetre is $\frac{1}{100}$ th of a metre.

The millimetre (mm) is used in plans and scale drawings. It is a very small unit of measurement in everyday use.

10 mm $= 1$ cm
1000 mm $= 1$ m

By using the millimetre in plans for building houses very large numbers occur but since the unit is so small there is no need to use a decimal point. The width of a door is about 750 mm.

An inch is about 25 mm.

The kilometre (km) is used to measure longer distances, e.g. the distance between towns.

1000 m $= 1$ km

A kilometre is about $\frac{5}{8}$ of a mile. Edinburgh is about 70 km from Glasgow.

The speed limit of 30 m.p.h. would be about 50 km/h.

AREA

Area tells us how much floor space is in a room. It tells us how many square carpet tiles will be needed to cover the floor.

6

The square centimetre (cm²) replaces the square inch. The diagram shows 10 cm².

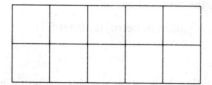

There are 10 000 cm² in a square metre.

The square metre (m²) is used to measure a room for a carpet. A large double bedroom would need about 20 m² of carpet.

To measure larger areas we would use the square kilometre (km²) or the hectare.

$$1 \text{ hectare} = 10\,000 \text{ m}^2$$

A football pitch is aout $\frac{1}{2}$ hectare.

WEIGHT

The gramme (g) is used to tell us the weight of a packet of sugar for example.

500 g is just over 1 lb or 16 oz.

The kilogram is used to measure our body weight. A petite young lady might weigh about 50 kg or 8 stone.

1000 g = 1 kg.

The tonne is used for weighing large amounts of coal for example.

1000 kg = 1 tonne.

The milligram (mg) is used for very small amounts, e.g. in tablets from the chemist.

1000 mg = 1 g.

VOLUME AND CAPACITY

The litre (l) has replaced the pint and gallon.

Petrol is bought in litres. A gallon of petrol is about 5 l.

$\frac{1}{2} l$ is just less than a pint.

The millilitre is used to tell us how much washing-up liquid is in a container, e.g. the average size container has about 750 ml of liquid.

Recipes use the millilitre, e.g. 1 tablespooon is about 15 ml and 1 teaspoon is about 5 ml.

1000 ml = 1 litre.

The size of a car's engine capacity is measured in cubic centimetres (cm^3). For example a 2 litre car is 2000 cm^3 in capacity.

1000 cm^3 = 1 l.

TEMPERATURE

Temperature is measured in degrees on the Centigrade or Celsius scales ($^\circ$ C) which replace the Fahrenheit scale ($^\circ$ F).

Water freezes at 0° C and boils at 100° C.

The water temperature of a car when heated up is about 70° C.

The normal body temperature is about 37° C.

TIME

Time by the 24 hour clock is given by the use of 4 digits, e.g. 0235. The first two digits tell the number of hours past midnight, the second two tell the number of minutes past the hour.

0235 is 2 hours past midnight and 35 minutes past the hour so it is 35 minutes after 2 o'clock in the morning, i.e. 2.35 a.m.

1435 means 2.35 p.m.

By the 12 hour clock a.m. means before noon and p.m. means after noon. Noon is 12 o'clock in the middle of the day. 12 o'clock at night is called midnight.

Days in the Month

The year starts in January and ends in December so the months are numbered from 1, for January, to 12, for December.

1.	January	31		7.	July	31
2.	February	28 (29 in a leap year)		8.	August	31
3.	March	31		9.	September	30
4.	April	30		10.	October	31
5.	May	31		11.	November	30
6.	June	30		12.	December	31

There are 365 days in a year, but every 4 years there is an extra day added to February giving 366 days in a leap year. The Olympic Games take place in leap years.

FACTORS AND H.C.F.'s

$P = \{2, 3, 5, 7, 11, 13, 17, 19, 23, 29, 31, \ldots\}$ is the set of prime numbers.

When 15 is written as 3×5 we say we have found the factors of 15 or factorised 15. The '3' and the '5' are both factors of 15. Since 3 and 5 are prime numbers we say we have found the prime factors of 15. A factor is a number than can be divided into another and leave no remainder, i.e. it can be divided evenly into that number.

The factors of 12 are 1, 2, 3, 4, 6, 12, that is,

$12 = 2 \times 6$ or $12 = 3 \times 4$ or $12 = 1 \times 12$.

PRIME FACTORS

There are often many ways of breaking a number into its factors but there is only one way of breaking it into its prime factors, e.g.

$12 = 2 \times 6 = 2 \times 2 \times 3$ $12 = 1 \times 12 = 2 \times 2 \times 3$ $12 = 3 \times 4 = 3 \times 2 \times 2$

9

Notice that in the last factorisation the '1' has been omitted because 1 is not a prime number. A prime number has no factors except for itself and 1, e.g. 37 = 1 × 37 only.

The order of the factors can be changed around, e.g. 12 = 3 × 4 = 12 = 4 × 3.

When the order of factors is changed around we are using what is known as the communative law, e.g. 3 × 4 = 4 × 3.

Numbers which are not prime are called composite numbers, i.e. numbers which can be factorised into their prime factors are composite, e.g. 12 = 3 × 2 × 2 is composite, 74 = 2 × 37 is composite.

The prime factors of a number may be found by successive division by successive prime numbers.

Example:

Find prime factors of 3740.

Since number is even 2 is a factor	2	3740
Since number is still even, 2 is a factor again	2	1870
3 is not but 5 must be	5	935
7 is not, so try 11	11	187
17 is prime	17	17
		1

When the quotient is 1, the factorisation is complete and the divisors are the prime factors, i.e. 3740 = 2 × 2 × 5 × 11 × 17.

COMMON FACTORS

Numbers such as 15 = 3 × 5 and 21 = 3 × 7 are said to have a common factor, i.e. 3, because 3 is a factor of both 15 and 21.

Numbers such as 30 = 2 × 3 × 5 and 42 = 2 × 3 × 7 have more than one common factor, i.e. 2 and 3. The product of the common factors is the highest common factor (H.C.F.) of the given numbers, e.g. 2 × 3 = 6 is the highest common factor of 30 and 42.

FRACTIONS

N = {1, 2, 3, 4, 5, 6, . . .} is the set of natural numbers.

A fraction has the form $\frac{\text{natural number}}{\text{natural number}}$, e.g. $\frac{2}{3}, \frac{1}{5}, \frac{99}{154}$

Fractions of this form are called vulgar fractions. When the top number (the numerator) is greater than the bottom number (the denominator) the fraction is called an improper fraction, e.g. $\frac{3}{2}, \frac{9}{4}, \frac{89}{73}, \frac{5}{1}$

Improper fractions of the form $\frac{5}{1}, \frac{9}{1}, \frac{79}{1}$ etc. are natural numbers 5, 9, 79 etc. respectively.

MULTIPLICATION OF FRACTIONS

Fractions may be multiplied by each other,

e.g. $\frac{2}{3} \times \frac{4}{5} = \frac{2 \times 4}{3 \times 5} = \frac{8}{15}$

$$\frac{2}{3} \times \frac{4}{5} \times \frac{7}{9} = \frac{2 \times 4 \times 7}{3 \times 5 \times 9} = \frac{8 \times 7}{15 \times 9} = \frac{56}{135}$$

EQUAL FRACTIONS

Fractions can be equal to each other, e.g. $\frac{1}{2} = \frac{2}{4}$

These are equal to each other because when the numerator and the denominator are multiplied by the same number then the value of the fraction is not changed $\frac{1}{2} = \frac{1 \times 2}{2 \times 2} = \frac{2}{4}$

Similarly $\frac{3}{4} = \frac{3 \times 5}{4 \times 5} = \frac{15}{20}$

Fractions may be treated in this way because in multiplying the numerator and the denominator by the same number, $\frac{2}{2}$ or $\frac{5}{5}$ etc., we are in fact multiplying the fraction by 1.

When any number is multiplied by 1 its value is unchanged. For this reason 1 is called the identity element for multiplication.

When the numerator and the denominator are divided by the same number then the value of the fraction is again unchanged, e.g. $\frac{2}{4}$ may be divided in the numerator and the denominator by 2 giving $\frac{1}{2}$ which we have seen is equal to $\frac{2}{4}$.

A fraction is said to be in its lowest terms if there is no common factor between the numerator and denominator, e.g. $\frac{2}{3}$ is in its lowest terms but $\frac{4}{6}$ is not because the numerator and the denominator have a common factor of 2, i.e. $\frac{4}{6} = \frac{2 \times 2}{2 \times 3} = \frac{2}{3}$.

What we have done is found the common factor between the numerator and the denominator then cancelled it out, i.e. the '2' was the common factor.

When two fractions are multiplied so that their product is equal to 1 then the two fractions are called multiplicative inverses of each other, or reciprocals of each other, e.g. $\frac{2}{3} \times \frac{3}{2} = \frac{6}{6} = 1$.

$\frac{2}{3}$ is the multiplicative inverse of $\frac{3}{2}$ and vice versa. Similarly $\frac{1}{3}$ is the reciprocal of 3 and vice versa.

The multiplicative inverse of a fraction enables the division of fractions to be done by multiplication! e.g. $\frac{2}{3} \div \frac{4}{9} = \frac{2}{3} \times \frac{9}{4} = \frac{2 \times 9}{3 \times 4} = \frac{2 \times 3 \times 3}{3 \times 2 \times 2} = \frac{3}{2}$, i.e. instead of dividing by $\frac{4}{9}$ we can multiply by $\frac{9}{4}$ which is the multiplicative inverse of $\frac{4}{9}$.

DIVISION OF FRACTIONS

The form $\frac{2}{3}$ means the same as $2 \div 3$ so too, $\dfrac{\frac{2}{3}}{\frac{4}{9}}$ means $\frac{2}{3} \div \frac{4}{9} = \frac{2}{3} \times \frac{9}{4} = \frac{3}{2}$ as before.

Similarly $\dfrac{\frac{2}{9} \times \frac{4}{5}}{\frac{2}{5} \times \frac{5}{3}} = \dfrac{\frac{8}{45}}{\frac{10}{15}} = \frac{8}{45} \div \frac{10}{15} = \frac{8}{45} \times \frac{15}{10} = \frac{4}{15}$

Finding a fraction of a whole number, e.g. $\frac{2}{3}$ of 90 is done by multiplication in the form $\frac{2}{3} \times \frac{90}{1} = \frac{2 \times 90}{3 \times 1} = 60$

Remember $90 = 90 \div 1 = \frac{90}{1}$

Finding a fraction of a fraction is accomplished by the same method, e.g.
$\frac{2}{3}$ of $\frac{5}{7} = \frac{2}{3} \times \frac{5}{7} = \frac{10}{21}$

IMPROPER (TOP HEAVY) FRACTIONS

An improper fraction may be changed to a mixed number by dividing the numerator by the denominator.

Example:

Change $\frac{3}{2}$ to a mixed number.

$2 \underline{|3}$ i.e. $\frac{3}{2} = 1\frac{1}{2}$, i.e. the quotient (the answer to the division) is
$\;\; 1\,r\,1$

the whole number, and the $\dfrac{\text{remainder}}{\text{divisor}}$ is the fraction.

Example:

Change $\frac{17}{5}$ to a mixed number.

$5 \underline{|17}$ i.e. $\frac{17}{5} = 3\frac{2}{5}$
$\;\; 3\,r\,2$

13

PERCENTAGES AND FRACTIONS

83% (83 per cent) means 83 per hundred, e.g. if a pupil scored 83 marks out of a possible hundred marks his mark could be written $\frac{83}{100}$ or 83%.

Similarly all percentages may be written in the form of a fraction,

e.g. $37\% = \frac{37}{100}$, $79\% = \frac{79}{100}$, $50\% = \frac{50}{100} = \frac{5 \times 10}{10 \times 10} = \frac{1}{2}$

Looking at this from another point of view all fractions may be expressed as percentages. This is done simply by multiplying the fraction by 100 and writing the percentage sign,

e.g. $\frac{1}{2} = \frac{1}{2} \times 100\% = \frac{100}{2}\% = 50\%$, $\frac{3}{4} = \frac{3}{4} \times 100\% = \frac{300}{4}\% = 75\%$ etc.

We can use the above knowledge to find percentages of any quantities.

Example:

Find 5% of 150

$$5\% \text{ of } 150 \Leftrightarrow \frac{5}{100} \text{ of } 150 \Leftrightarrow \frac{5}{100} \times 150 = \frac{15}{2} = 7\frac{1}{2}$$

Example:

Find $2\frac{1}{2}\%$ of £300

$$2\frac{1}{2}\% \text{ of } £300 \Leftrightarrow £\frac{\frac{5}{2}}{100} \times 300$$

$$\Leftrightarrow £\frac{5 \times 300}{2 \times 100} = £\frac{15}{2}$$

$$= £7\frac{1}{2} = £7.50$$

CHANGING FRACTIONS TO DECIMALS

Any fraction may be changed to decimal form by dividing the numerator by the denominator, e.g. $\frac{1}{2} = 0.5$. The working is as follows:

$2\left\lfloor\frac{1 \cdot 0}{0 \cdot 5}\right.$. The method is to write down the numerator, place a decimal point

14

after it then put a zero after the point. Now lay out a division arrangement, put a decimal point in the space for the answer under the decimal point already there. Divide by the denominator.

Example:

Express $\frac{3}{4}$ in decimal form.

$$4 \overline{\left)\begin{array}{l} 3\cdot00 \\ \hline 0\cdot75 \end{array}\right.} \quad \text{i.e.} \quad \frac{3}{4} = 0\cdot75$$

Notice that more zeros can be used as required until there is no 'carry over' figure or till the necessary number of decimal places is reached.

CHANGING DECIMALS TO PERCENTAGES

Decimal fractions are converted to percentages as before

i.e. by multiplying by 100, e.g. $0\cdot75 = 0\cdot75 \times 100\% = 75\%$ and writing the percentage sign.

$0\cdot5$ is $0\cdot5 \times 100\% = 50\%$

MULTIPLES AND L.C.M.s

A = $\{2, 4, 6, 8, 10, \ldots\ldots\ldots\ldots\ldots\ldots\ldots\ldots\}$ is the set of multiples of 2
B = $\{3, 6, 9, 12, 15, \ldots\ldots\ldots\ldots\ldots\ldots\ldots\}$ is the set of multiples of 3
C = $\{5, 10, 15, 20, 25, \ldots\ldots\ldots\ldots\ldots\ldots\}$ is the set of multiples of 5

A number which is a multiple of 2 has a factor of 2
A number which is a multiple of 3 has a factor of 3
A number which is a multiple of 5 has a factor of 5

  6 is a multiple of 2 and a multiple of 3
12 is a multiple of 2 and a multiple of 3
18 is a multiple of 2 and a multiple of 3 and so on

The '6' above is special, because it is the lowest common multiple of 2 and 3, i.e. the lowest number which has a factor of both 2 and 3.

The lowest common multiple (L.C.M.) of two prime numbers is their product.

The lowest common multiple of any number of different prime numbers is their product, e.g. the lowest common multiple of 2, 3 and 5 is $2 \times 3 \times 5 = 30$.

The lowest common multiple of two numbers which are not both prime is the product of their different prime factors, e.g. the L.C.M of 6 and 3 is $2 \times 3 = 6$. The L.C.M. of 6 and 3 and 15 is $2 \times 3 \times 5 = 30$.

However if a prime factor appears more than once in any of the numbers as in $9 = 3 \times 3$. Then the L.C.M. of 6 and 9, for example, is $2 \times 3 \times 3 = 18$.

Similarly the L.C.M. of 8 and 9 is $2 \times 2 \times 2 \times 3 \times 3 = 72$.

The next section will explain the method further.

POWERS AND INDICES

2×2 can be represented by 2^2 (2 to the power of 2) **or** 2 squared

$2 \times 2 \times 2$ can be represented by 2^3 (2 to the power of 3) **or** 2 cubed

$2 \times 2 \times 2 \times 2$ can be represented by 2^4 (2 to the power of 4)

$a \times a \times a$ can be represented by a^3 (a to the power of 3)

In this last example we say that we have raised a to the power 3. 'a' is called the base and '3' the index.

The base tells what factors we are dealing with and the index tells how many of these factors there are, e.g. 4^3 means we are dealing with factors of 4, and that there are 3 of these factors. Hence $4^3 = 4 \times 4 \times 4 = 64$.

Earlier we found that the L.C.M. of 8 and 9 was $2 \times 2 \times 2 \times 3 \times 3 = 72$.

We can now write the L.C.M. in a neater form, namely, $2^3 \times 3^2 = 72$.

We are now able to state that the L.C.M. of a set of numbers is the product of the highest powers of their different prime factors.

e.g. the L.C.M. of 8, 9 and 12 is found by writing the prime factors of these numbers, i.e.

$$8 = 2 \times 2 \times 2 = 2^3$$
$$9 = 3 \times 3 \quad\quad = 3^2$$
$$12 = 3 \times 2 \times 2 = 3 \times 2^2$$

16

Now the different prime factors are 2 and 3 and the highest power of 2 is 2^3, and the highest power of 3 is 3^2 so the L.C.M. $= 2^3 \times 3^2 = 72$.

Similarly the L.C.M. of 5, 9, 15 and 6 can be found as follows:

> 5 is prime
> $9 = 3^2$
> $15 = 3 \times 5$
> $6 = 2 \times 3$

> So the L.C.M. is $2 \times 3^2 \times 5 = 90$.

ORDERED FRACTIONS

Fractions may be ordered into ascending or descending order of magnitude by converting them to the same denominator. This denominator will be the L.C.M. of the existing denominators.

Example:

$\frac{2}{5}, \frac{3}{4}, \frac{5}{9}, \frac{2}{3}$ in ascending order of magnitude.

> L.C.M. of denominators 5, 4, 9, 3 = 180.

> $\frac{2}{5} = \frac{72}{180}, \frac{3}{4} = \frac{135}{180}, \frac{5}{9} = \frac{100}{180}, \frac{2}{3} = \frac{120}{180}$

> Ascending order of magnitude is $\frac{72}{180}, \frac{100}{180}, \frac{120}{180}, \frac{135}{180}$

> i.e. $\frac{2}{5}, \frac{5}{9}, \frac{2}{3}, \frac{3}{4}$

For descending order of magnitude the order is reversed to

> $\frac{3}{4}, \frac{2}{3}, \frac{5}{9}, \frac{2}{5}$

SIMPLE INTEREST

The formula for finding the simple interest is

$$I = \frac{P \times R \times T}{100} = \frac{PRT}{100} \text{ where}$$

I stands for interest in £'s
P stands for principal (i.e. sum of money invested) in £'s
R stands for rate of interest per annum
T stands for time in years or fractions of a year.

Example:

Find the simple interest on £150 at 5% per annum for 2 years.

$$I = £\frac{150 \times 5 \times 2}{100} = £15$$

Example:

Find the simple interest on £150 at 5% per annum for 2 years 6 months.

$$I = £\frac{150 \times 5 \times 5}{100 \times 2} = £\frac{75}{4} = £18.75$$

(Notice that 2 years 6 months is $2\frac{1}{2}$ years $= \frac{5}{2}$ years.)

Example:

Find the simple interest on £150 at $2\frac{1}{2}$% per annum for $3\frac{1}{2}$ years.

$$I = £\frac{150 \times 5 \times 7}{100 \times 2 \times 2} = £\frac{105}{8} = £13.125 = £13.12 \text{ to nearest 1p.}$$

COMPOUND INTEREST

To calculate compound interest the same formula as that for simple interest $I = \frac{PRT}{100}$ is used for each year, so T is always equal to 1.

The principal each year is made up from the previous year's principal plus the interest gained that year. In Compound Interest the interest is calculated only on a whole number of £'s.

18

Example:

Find the compound interest on £1750 for 3 years at 5% per annum.

P (1st year) = £1750

$$I \text{ (1st year)} = £\frac{1750 \times 5 \times 1}{100} = £\frac{8750}{100} = £87.50$$

P (2nd year) = £1750 + 87.50 = £1837.50

$$I \text{ (2nd year)} = £\frac{1837 \times 5 \times 1}{100} = £\frac{9182}{100} = £91.85$$

P (3rd year) = £1837.50 + £91.85 = £1929.35

$$I \text{ (3rd year)} = £\frac{1929 \times 5 \times 1}{100} = £\frac{9645}{100} = £96.45$$

Amount after 3 years   = £1929.35 + £96.45 = £2025.80

Total interest after 3 years = £2025.80 – £1750 = £275.80

It may be advantageous not to cancel the factors in calculating the interest each year, for with a denominator of 100 the division is simply a matter of shifting the position of the decimal point,

$$\text{e.g. } I = £\frac{218.51 \times 3 \times 1}{100} = £\frac{655.53}{100} = £6.56 \text{ to nearest 1p.}$$

STANDARD FORM or SCIENTIFIC NOTATION

To express a number in standard form or scientific notation it must be put in the shape $a \times 10^n$ where a is a number greater than or equal to 1 and less than 10, i.e. $1 \leqslant a < 10$, and n is a member of the set of integers, Z.

$$Z = \{.................... -3, -2, -1, 0, 1, 2, 3, ... \}$$

19

Example:

Express 13·2 in standard form $\qquad$ $13·2 = 1·32 \times 10^1$

'*a*' is found by placing a decimal point after the first digit in the number which is not zero. This is called the standard position for the decimal point.

'*n*' is found by counting the number of places this new position has moved the decimal point from its original position.

If the original number was greater than 1 then '*n*' is a positive number.

If the original number was less than 1 then '*n*' is a negative number.

Examples:

$153 = 1·53 \times 10^2$ $\qquad$ (Note that when the number is a whole number we assume the point to be after the last digit, i.e. 153.)

$0·153 = 1·53 \times 10^{-1}$
$0·0153 = 1·53 \times 10^{-2}$
$153000 = 1·53 \times 10^5$ $\qquad$ (When the decimal point is in its standard position then the number remains as it stands.)
$1·53 = 1·53$

ROUNDING OFF AND SIGNIFICANT FIGURES

A. Numbers greater than 1.

Examples:

Round off the following numbers to 3 significant figures.

(a) 1579 $\rightarrow$ 1580 to 3 s.f. (3 significant figures)
15·781 $\rightarrow$ 15·8 to 3 s.f.

If the digit after the third figure is greater than 5 then the third digit is increased by 1.

(b) 157·39 $\rightarrow$ 157 to 3 s.f.
1·574 $\rightarrow$ 1·57 to 3 s.f.

If the digit after the third figure is less than 5 then the third digit is unaltered.

20

(c) 1575 → 1580 to 3 s.f.
1585 → 1580 to 3 s.f.

If the digit after the third figure is a 5 then the third digit must be even.
If the third digit is already even it remains unaltered, but if the third digit is odd then it is increased by 1.

(d) 1575·1 → 1580 to 3 s.f.
15750 → 15800 to 3 s.f.
158501 → 159000 to 3 s.f.

If there is another non zero digit after the 5 then we revert to type *(a)* above.

Note that there must be the same number of digits before and after rounding off a whole number,

e.g. 15 739 has 5 digits and after round off to 3 s.f., i.e. 15 700 there are still 5 digits, but zeros only after the point are omitted, e.g. 157·39 is 157 to 3 s.f.

B. Numbers less than 1.

Examples:

Round off the following numbers to 3 s.f.

(a) 0·1579   → 0·158 to 3 s.f.
0·15781   → 0·158 to 3 s.f.

(b) 0·015739   → 0·0157 to 3 s.f.
0·001574   → 0·00157 to 3 s.f.

(c) 0·0001575 → 0·000158 to 3 s.f.
0·00001585 → 0·0000158 to 3 s.f.

(d) 0·15751   → 0·158 to 3 s.f.
0·157502   → 0·158 to 3 s.f.
0·1585001   → 0·159 to 3 s.f.

C. Rounding off to decimal places.

The previous rules apply but only the digits after the decimal point are considered.

Example:

Round off the following numbers to 3 d.p. (i.e. 3 decimal places).

$87\cdot6734 \rightarrow 87\cdot673$ to 3 d.p.

$87\cdot0647 \rightarrow 87\cdot065$ to 3 d.p.

$87\cdot0065 \rightarrow 87\cdot006$ to 3 d.p.

$87\cdot0007 \rightarrow 87\cdot001$ to 3 d.p.

$87\cdot0003 \rightarrow 87\cdot000$ to 3 d.p.

Notice that $87\cdot000$ units of measurement is different from 87 units, for $87\cdot000$ km, say, indicates that the measurement taken is 1000 times more accurate than that given as 87 km, i.e. $87\cdot000$ km has been measured to the nearest metre $\left(\frac{1}{1000}\text{ of a km}\right)$, but 87 km means that the measurement has been taken only to the nearest km.

AVERAGE SPEED, TIME AND DISTANCE

The average speed is calculated by the ratio (i.e. fraction form)

$$\frac{\text{total distance covered}}{\text{total time taken}}$$

e.g. A train leaves at 0830 h and arrives at 1230 h. If it has travelled 384 km what was its average speed over the journey?

Total distance $= 384$ km
Total time $= 4$ h
Average speed $= \frac{384}{4}$ km/h $= 96$ km/h (i.e. 96 km per h).

Since distance, speed and time over a journey are all related then if any two quantities are known the third can be found. The formulae are as follows:

(i) Average speed = $\dfrac{\text{total distance covered}}{\text{total time taken}}$

(ii) Total distance covered = average speed × total time taken.

(iii) Total time taken = $\dfrac{\text{total distance covered}}{\text{average speed}}$

Example:

Find the distance covered by a car travelling at an average speed of 48 km/h if the time taken is 30 min.

$$\text{Distance} = (48 \times \tfrac{1}{2}) \text{ km} = 24 \text{ km}$$

Notice that the speed was given in km/h so the time 30 min had to be converted to $\tfrac{1}{2}$ hour.

Example:

Find the time taken to cover 192 km at an average speed of 12 km/h, if no stops were made on the journey.

$$\text{Time taken} = \frac{192}{12} \text{ h} = 16 \text{ h}$$

Example:

Find the time taken to cover 192 km if the first half of the journey is made at 24 km/h and then a 15 min break is taken, the next 24 km made at 30 km/hr and a break of 5 min is taken and the last part of the journey at 32 km/h.

Time for first part of journey $= \dfrac{96}{24} \text{ h} = 4 \text{ h}$

Time for second part of journey $= \dfrac{24}{30} \text{ h} = 0 \cdot 8 \text{ h} = 48 \text{ min.}$

Time for third part of journey $= \dfrac{72}{32} \text{ h} = 2\tfrac{1}{4} \text{ h} = 2 \text{ h } 15 \text{ min.}$

Total time = (4 h + 48 min + 2 h 15 min + 15 min + 5 min
           = 7 h 23 min

ADDITION AND SUBTRACTION WITH FRACTIONS

A mixed number can be changed to an improper fraction as follows:

$$3\frac{1}{2} = 3 + \frac{1}{2}$$

$$= \left(3 \times \frac{2}{2}\right) + \frac{1}{2}$$

$$= \frac{6}{2} + \frac{1}{2} \text{ (i.e. 6 halves + 1 half)}$$

$$= \frac{7}{2} \text{ (i.e. 7 halves)}$$

Notice that $\frac{6}{2} + \frac{1}{2} = \frac{7}{2}$ is the same as

$$\frac{6+1}{2} = \frac{7}{2}$$

The aim is to change the whole number into an improper fraction of the same type as the other fraction. In the above example the '3' was changed to $\frac{6}{2}$. Similarly,

$$7\frac{3}{4} = 7 + \frac{3}{4}$$

$$= \left(7 \times \frac{4}{4}\right) + \frac{3}{4} \left(\text{Remember } 7 \times \frac{4}{4} = 7 \times 1 = 7\right)$$

$$= \frac{28}{4} + \frac{3}{4}$$

$$= \frac{28+3}{4}$$

$$= \frac{31}{4}$$

We can extend this idea to add such as

$$\frac{3}{5} + \frac{7}{10}$$

$$\Leftrightarrow \left(\frac{3}{5} \times \frac{2}{2}\right) + \frac{7}{10}$$

$$\Leftrightarrow \frac{6}{10} + \frac{7}{10}$$

$$\Leftrightarrow \frac{6+7}{10}$$

$$\Leftrightarrow \frac{13}{10} = 1\frac{3}{10} \text{ (or } 1\cdot3 \text{ in decimal form)}$$

Fractions are easily added if they have the same denominators. If they do not have the same denominators then we change their form so that they do.

$$\text{e.g. } \frac{3}{5} + \frac{2}{3} \Leftrightarrow \frac{9}{15} + \frac{10}{15} \Leftrightarrow \frac{9+10}{15} = \frac{19}{15} = 1\frac{4}{15}$$

Most of the steps may be omitted if we use the L.C.M. of the denominators, e.g. the L.C.M. of 5 and 3 is 15, thus

$$\frac{3}{5} + \frac{2}{3} = \frac{9+10}{15} = \frac{19}{15} = 1\frac{4}{15}$$

Examples:

(a) $\frac{5}{8} + \frac{7}{12} = \frac{15+14}{24} = \frac{29}{24} = 1\frac{5}{24}$

(b) $1\frac{5}{8} + 3\frac{7}{12} = 4 + \frac{15+14}{24} = 4 + \frac{29}{24}$

$$= 4 + 1\frac{5}{24}$$

$$= 5\frac{5}{24}$$

Remember $1\frac{5}{8} = 1 + \frac{5}{8}$ and $3\frac{7}{12} = 3 + \frac{7}{12}$

so $1 + \frac{5}{8} + 3 + \frac{7}{12} = 4 + \frac{5}{8} + \frac{7}{12}$

(c) $\frac{5}{8} - \frac{7}{12} = \frac{15-14}{24} = \frac{1}{24}$

(d) $2\frac{5}{8} - 1\frac{7}{12} = 2 + \frac{5}{8} - \left(1 + \frac{7}{12}\right)$

$$= 2 + \frac{5}{8} - 1 - \frac{7}{12}$$

$$= (2 - 1) + \frac{5}{8} - \frac{7}{12}$$

$$= 1 + \frac{15 - 14}{24} = 1 + \frac{1}{24}$$

$$= 1\frac{1}{24}$$

(e) $2\frac{5}{8} + 1\frac{7}{12} - 1\frac{1}{3} = (2 + 1 - 1) + \frac{5}{8} + \frac{7}{12} - \frac{1}{3}$

$$= 2 + \frac{15 + 14 - 8}{24}$$

$$= 2 + \frac{21}{24}$$

$$= 2\frac{7}{8}$$

Addition and multiplication may be combined as in
$$3(4 + 5) \text{ i.e. } 3 \times (4 + 5) \text{ or } 3 \times 9 = 27.$$

Again $\frac{3}{3}\left(\frac{1}{2} + \frac{1}{4}\right)$ i.e. $\frac{3}{4} \times \frac{3}{4} = \frac{9}{16}$

The above can be done by using the distributive law, i.e. by multiplying each number in the brackets by the one outside

i.e. $3(4 + 5) = 3 \times 4 + 3 \times 5$

$$= 12 + 15$$

$$= 27 \text{ as before.}$$

and $\frac{3}{4}\left(\frac{1}{2} + \frac{1}{4}\right) = \frac{3}{4} \times \frac{1}{2} + \frac{3}{4} \times \frac{1}{4}$

$$= \frac{3}{8} + \frac{3}{16}$$

$$= \frac{6 + 3}{16}$$

$$= \frac{9}{16} \text{ as before.}$$

Because these two ways give the same results we say that multiplication is distributive over addition.

PERIMETERS

A perimeter is the distance round the edge of any given shape.

The perimeter of a rectangle is $2(l + b)$ or $2l + 2b$

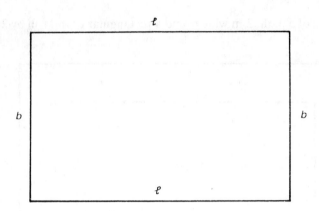

Here l stands for length and b for breadth.

The perimeter of a square is $4l$ since in a square $l = b$.

The perimeter of a circle is $2\pi r$ or πd, r being the radius and d the diameter. $d = 2r$.

π is constant $\left(\dfrac{22}{7} \text{ or } 3 \cdot 14 \text{ approx.}\right)$

The perimeter of a circle is usually referred to as the circumference.

The perimeter of any plane figure is the sum of the lengths of its boundary lines.

AREAS AND VOLUMES

The area of a rectangle is (length × breadth) units^2.

In formula form $A = l \times b$ or $A = lb$.

Example:

Find the area of a path, 2 m wide round a rectangular lawn 11 m by 20 m.

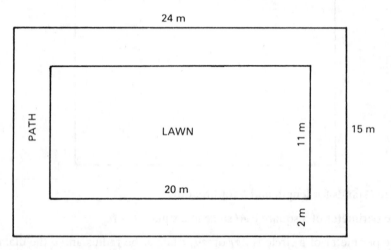

Always draw a sketch where possible. Always ensure that l and b are in the same units of measurement. The area of the path will be the area of the outside rectangle minus the area of the lawn.

Area of outside rectangle	$= (24 \times 15) \text{ m}^2$	$= 360 \text{ m}^2$
Area of lawn	$= (20 \times 11) \text{ m}^2$	$= 220 \text{ m}^2$
Area of path	$= (360 - 220) \text{ m}^2$	
	$= 140 \text{ m}^2$	

Example:

Find the length of a lawn of area 220 m^2 if it is 10 m broad.

$$l = \frac{A}{b} = \frac{220}{10} \text{ m} = 22 \text{ m}.$$

Example:

How many turfs of grass each 30 cm square are needed to cover a lawn 6 m by 12 m?

In any 'tiling' problem such as this first find the area to be covered then find the area of each tile in the same units of area, thus

Number of tiles $= \dfrac{\text{area to be covered}}{\text{area of tile}}$

Number of turfs $= \dfrac{\text{area of lawn}}{\text{area of turf}}$

Area of lawn $= 6 \times 12 \text{ m}^2$
$= 72 \text{ m}^2$

Area of turf $= \dfrac{3}{10} \times \dfrac{3}{10} \text{ m}^2$

$= \dfrac{9}{100} \text{ m}^2$

Number of turfs $= \dfrac{72}{\frac{9}{100}}$

$= 72 \times \dfrac{100}{9} = 800$

The area of a triangle is $\dfrac{1}{2}$ (base $\times$ height) units^2

In formula form $\quad A = \dfrac{1}{2} bh$

Example:

Find the area of a triangular metal plate whose base is 5 cm and height 4 cm. Find also the cost if the metal is 3p per cm^2.

$A \quad = \dfrac{1}{2} \times 5 \times 4 \text{ cm}^2$

$= 10 \text{ cm}^2$

Cost $= (10 \times 3)\text{p}$

$= 30\text{p}$

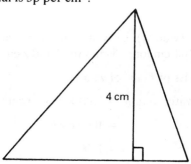

4 cm

Notice that any side of a triangle may be considered to be the base, but once the base is decided then the height must be the perpendicular distance to this base from the opposite vertex. The height of a triangle may be referred to as the altitude of the triangle.

Example:

Find the length of the base of a triangle whose area is 40 cm^2 and whose altitude is 6 cm.

$$b = \frac{2A}{h} = \frac{2 \times 40}{6} \text{ cm} = \frac{40}{3} \text{ cm} = 13\frac{1}{3} \text{ cm}.$$

A solid with a shape like a matchbox is called a cuboid. The volume or capacity of a cuboid is given by the formula $V = lbh$.

Example:

Find the volume of a rectangular box 10 cm long, 5 cm broad and 2 cm high.

$$V = 10 \times 5 \times 2 \text{ cm}^3$$
$$= 100 \text{ cm}^3$$

Again all dimensions, i.e. l, b, h, must be in the same unit of measurement before using the formula.

When the length, breadth and height are all equal then the shape is called a cube such as a die. The volume of a cube is then given by $V = l^3$.

Example:

Find the mass (weight) of water in a rectangular tank, whose inside dimensions are 100 cm long, 5 cm broad and 2 cm high.

(1 g is the mass of 1 cm^3 of water)

Volume of water in tank $= (100 \times 5 \times 2) \text{ cm}^3$

$= 1000 \text{ cm}^3$

Mass of water $= 1000 \text{ g}$

$= 1 \text{ kg}$

Shapes such as the cuboid, cylinder and triangular prism are all called prisms. The volume of such a prism is $V = $ (area of base $\times$ height) units^3.

Example:

Find the volume of a cylinder 10 cm long and diameter 4 cm.

Area of base $= \pi r^2$

$V = (\pi \times 2^2 \times 10) \text{ cm}^3$

$\quad = 40\,\pi \text{ cm}^3$

Example:

Find the volume of a triangular prism 10 cm long and with equilateral triangular faces of side 4 cm.

$V = \left(\frac{1}{2} \times 4 \times 2\sqrt{3} \times 10\right) \text{ cm}^3$

$\quad = 40\sqrt{3} \text{ cm}^3$

If the accuracy of the answers is not specified, e.g. correct to 3 s.f. or 2 d.p., then there is no need to calculate 40π or $40\sqrt{3}$ in the last 2 examples.

Example:

Find the surface area of a closed box 10 cm $\times$ 5 cm $\times$ 2 cm.

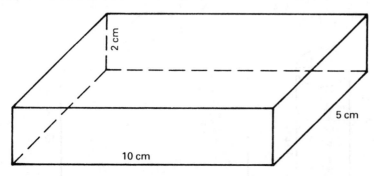

There are 6 faces with opposite pairs equal in area. Each face is a rectangle.

Surface are $= [2(10 \times 5) + 2(10 \times 2) + 2(5 \times 2)] \text{ cm}^2$

$\quad\quad = (100 + 40 + 20) \text{ cm}^2$

$\quad\quad = 160 \text{ cm}^2$

Example:

Find the surface area of a triangular prism 10 cm long with equilateral triangular sides of 4 cm correct to 2 d.p.

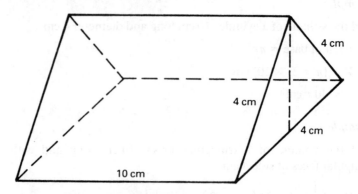

Area of 3 rectangular faces $= 3(10 \times 4)$ cm^2
$\qquad\qquad\qquad\qquad\qquad\ = 120$ cm^2
Area of 2 triangular faces $\ = 2(\frac{1}{2} \times 4 \times 2\sqrt{3}\,)$ cm^2
$\qquad\qquad\qquad\qquad\qquad\ = 8\sqrt{3}$ cm^2
Total surface area $\qquad\quad = (120 + 13 \cdot 84)$ cm^2
$\qquad\qquad\qquad\qquad\qquad\ = 133 \cdot 84$ cm^2 to 2 d.p.

Example:

Find the total surface area of a closed cylinder 10 cm high and diameter 4 cm.

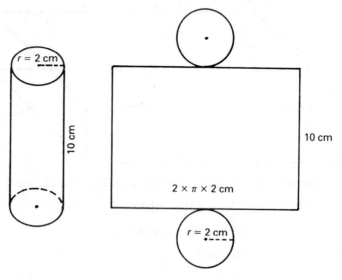

32

Area of two circular sections $= (2 \times \pi 2^2)$ cm^2

$= 8\pi$ cm^2

Area of curved surface $= (10 \times 2\pi 2)$ cm^2

$= 40\pi$ cm^2

Total surface area $= (40\pi + 8\pi)$ cm^2

$= 48\pi$ cm^2

Notice that the curved surface of the cylinder can be slit open and placed flat in the form of a rectangle whose width is the same as the circumference of the circular sections.

Example:

Find the area of a rectangular field 20 m × 30 m with semi-circular sections on the narrower sides. Find also its perimeter.

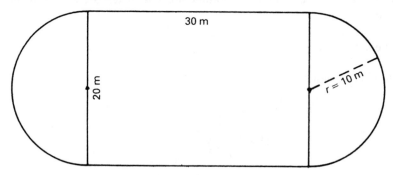

Area of rectangular section $= (20 \times 30)$ m^2

$= 600$ m^2

Area of sum of two semi-circular sections $= \pi 10^2$ m^2

$= 100\pi$ m^2

Total area $(600 + 100\pi)$ m^2

$= 600 + 314$ m^2

$= 914$ m^2

Perimeter $= (2 \times 30 + 2 \times \pi \times 10)$ m

$= (60 + 62{\cdot}8)$ m

$= 122{\cdot}8$ m

Example:

Find the radius of a circle of area 66 cm^2 $\left(\text{Take } \pi = \frac{22}{7}\right)$

Area of circle $= \pi r^2$

$$r = \sqrt{\frac{A}{\pi}}$$

$$= \sqrt{\frac{66}{\pi}} \text{ cm}$$

$$= \sqrt{\frac{66 \times 7}{22}} \text{ cm}$$

$$= \sqrt{21} \text{ cm}$$

Example:

Find the height of a cylinder of volume 462 cm^3 when the radius of the base is 7 cm.

$$\left(\text{Take } \pi = \frac{22}{7} \text{ cm}\right)$$

Volume of cylinder $= \pi r^2 h$

$$h = \frac{V}{\pi r^2}$$

$$= \frac{462 \times 7}{22 \times 7 \times 7} \text{ cm}$$

$$= 3 \text{ cm}$$

SQUARE ROOTS

There are several ways of finding the square root of a number. Some of these are found below. The method employed depends on the accuracy required and the nature of the number.

1. By factors and tables
    $$\sqrt{36} = \sqrt{4 \times 9} = \sqrt{4} \times \sqrt{9} = 2 \times 3 = 6$$

    The steps illustrate the method but it would be obvious from the knowledge of the first few elements of the set of square numbers that $\sqrt{36} = 6$

A = {1, 4, 9, 16, 25, 36, 49, 64, 81, ...} is the set of square numbers.

The first step is to factorise the number finding any square factors where possible but these might not be obvious.

Example:

Find $\sqrt{432}$ correct to 3 s.f.

$\sqrt{432} = \sqrt{4 \times 108} = \sqrt{4 \times 4 \times 27} = \sqrt{16 \times 9 \times 3}$

$\quad = \sqrt{16} \times \sqrt{9} \times \sqrt{3}$

$\quad = 4 \times 3 \times \sqrt{3}$

$\quad = 12\sqrt{3}$

$\quad = 12 \times 1.73$ (from square root tables)

$\quad = 20.76$

$\quad = 20.8$ to 3 s.f.

Notice that the square root tables give values of root of numbers from 1 to 100 3 s.f., so numbers must be factorised into $a \times 100$ or $a \times \frac{1}{100}$ where $1 \leqslant a \leqslant 100$.

Alternatively $\sqrt{432} = \sqrt{4.32 \times 100}$

$\quad\quad\quad = \sqrt{4.32} \times \sqrt{100}$

$\quad\quad\quad = 2.08 \times 10$ (from tables)

$\quad\quad\quad = 20.8$ to 3 s.f.

Example:

Find $\sqrt{4320}$ to 3 s.f.

$\sqrt{4320} \quad = \sqrt{43.2 \times 100}$

$\quad\quad\quad = \sqrt{43.2} \times \sqrt{100}$

$\quad\quad\quad = 6.57 \times 10$ (from tables)

$\quad\quad\quad = 65.7$ to 3 s.f.

Example:

Find $\sqrt{0\cdot432}$ to 3 s.f.

$$\sqrt{0\cdot432} = \sqrt{\frac{43\cdot2}{100}}$$

$$= \frac{\sqrt{43\cdot2}}{10}$$

$$= \frac{6\cdot57}{10}$$

$$= 0\cdot657 \text{ to 3 s.f.}$$

Example:

Find $\sqrt{0\cdot0432}$ to 3 s.f.

$$\sqrt{0\cdot0432} = \sqrt{\frac{4\cdot32}{100}}$$

$$= \frac{\sqrt{4\cdot32}}{10}$$

$$= \frac{2\cdot08}{10}$$

$$= 0\cdot208 \text{ to 3 s.f.}$$

For larger numbers we may have to employ 10000

Example:

Find $\sqrt{43192}$ to 3 s.f.

$$\sqrt{43192} = \sqrt{4\cdot3192 \times 10000}$$

$$= \sqrt{4\cdot32} \times \sqrt{10000}$$

$$= 2\cdot08 \times 100$$

$$= 208 \text{ to 3 s.f.}$$

2. By iteration.

If a number is divided by its square root then the quotient (answer to the division sum) will also be the square root, e.g. $3\overline{\smash{)}9}$ since $\sqrt{9} = 3$.

36

If a number is divided by one less than its square root then the quotient

will be greater than the square root, e.g. $2\overline{\smash{\big)}9}$ is $4\cdot5$.

The real square root will lie between the divisor (number we divide by) and the quotient. We use these facts to find the square roots by an iterative process.

Example:

Find the square root of 127 to 3 s.f. We know that the root will be just over 11 since 11 × 11 = 121 so we choose 11 as the first divisor.

```
     11·54
11 ) 127·0
     11
     17
     11
     60
     55
     50
     44
```

Now find the mean (average) of the divisor and quotient, i.e. $\dfrac{11 + 11\cdot54}{2}$

$$= 11\cdot27$$
$$= 11\cdot3 \text{ to 3 s.f.}$$

11·3 is used as the new divisor.

```
      11·23
113 ) 1270
      113
      140
      113
      270
      226
      440
```

Again find the mean of the divisor and the quotient $\dfrac{11\cdot3 + 11\cdot23}{2}$

$$= 11\cdot265$$
$$= 11\cdot3 \text{ to 3 s.f.}$$

When the first estimate is fairly accurate then one division will give the root correct to 3 s.f. as may be seen from the last example.

An accuracy to 5 s.f. may be obtained if the first approximation is taken from the table of square roots followed by one division.

ACCOUNTS FOR ELECTRICITY OR GAS

The method for such accounts is standard. First calculate the amount used by subtracting 'previous meter reading' from 'present meter reading'.

Next, consult tariff (i.e. table of charges) as the charge per unit usually depends on the amount used, e.g. the charge for the first 100 units used may be more than for any subsequent units.

Calculate total charge.

Check if there is any standing charge. (If so then add to calculated charge.)

Example:

Calculate the charge for electricity when the present meter reading is 15 000 units and the previous reading was 12 500 units when the cost is 3p per unit for the first 80 units and 1p per unit for the remainder.

Number of units $= 15\,000 - 12\,500 = 2\,500$

Cost of first 80 units $\quad = 80 \times 3p = £2.40$

Number of remaining units $= 2\,500 - 80 = 2420$

Cost of remaining units $\quad = £24.20$

Total cost $= £24.20 + £2.40 = £26.60$

PROFIT AND LOSS

If the selling price of goods is greater than the cost price then the dealer makes a profit.

i.e. profit = selling price – cost price.

If the selling price of goods is less than the cost price then the dealer makes a loss.

i.e. loss = cost price – selling price.

Example:

Find the profit or loss on 25 construction kits costing 50p each, 5 of which became unfit for sale but the remainder sold at 60p each.

cost price $\quad = (25 \times 50)p = £12.50$

selling price $= (20 \times 60)p = £12.00$

Since selling price is less than cost price there is a loss.

Loss $= £12.50 - £12.00$

$\quad = 50p$

38

PERCENTAGE PROFIT AND LOSS

Traders calculate their profit or loss as a percentage of either the cost price or the selling price. If the percentage profit or loss does not state whether it is on the cost price or the selling price, then assume it is on the cost price.

$$\text{percentage profit} = \left(\frac{\text{profit}}{\text{cost price}} \times 100 \right)\%$$

Again ensure that profit and cost price or selling price are in the same units.

Example:

Find the percentage profit or loss on goods costing £1.20 which sold at £1.40.

Since selling price is greater than cost price a profit was made.

$$\text{profit} = £1.40 - £1.20 = 20p$$

$$\% \text{ profit} = \frac{20}{120} \times 100\%$$

$$= \frac{100}{6}\% = 16\frac{2}{3}\%$$

Example:

50 copies of a mathematics book were bought for 90p each. The bookseller wished to make a profit of 20%. Find the total selling price and the selling price per copy.

$$\text{Total cost price} = (50 \times 90)p = £45$$

$$\text{Profit} = £\left(\frac{20}{100} \times 45 \right)$$

$$= £9$$

$$\text{Total selling price} = £45 + £9$$

$$= £54$$

$$\text{Selling price per copy} = £\frac{54}{50}$$

$$= £1.08$$

HIRE PURCHASE AND DISCOUNT

Goods may be purchased by paying cash or by paying a deposit then an amount per month.

The second method is called buying by hire purchase and is usually more expensive than by paying cash.

Example:

Find the cost of buying a coloured T.V. set costing £230 by hire purchase, with the terms £50 deposit and £8.50 per month over 2 years, i.e. 24 monthly payments of £8.50.

$$\text{Hire purchase cost} = £50 + £(24 \times 8.50)$$
$$= £50 + £204$$
$$= £254$$

Example:

If the previous set is sold at a discount of 5% for cash, how much will the customer pay? How much will he have saved by not buying by hire purchase?

$$\text{Discount} = £\left(\frac{5}{100} \times 230\right)$$
$$= £11.50$$

Cost of set = £230 – £11.50 = £218.50

$$\text{Saving} = £254 – £218.50$$
$$= £35.50$$

RATIO AND SCALES

When amounts of the same type are compared then a ratio of one amount to the other is found.

e.g. If one candidate in an election gains 6000 votes and another 4000 votes then the ratio of the number of votes is

$$\frac{6000}{4000} = \frac{3}{2} \text{ or } 3:2 \text{ (Read as 3 is to 2)}$$

If in the next election the first candidate increased his votes in the ratio 5:3 then the number of votes he gained in the second election was

$$\frac{5}{3} \times 6000 = 10\,000$$

In the form $a:b$ notice that a is the numerator and b the denominator of the form $\frac{a}{b}$.

Amounts changed in the ratio $\frac{a}{b}$ give the new amount simply by multiplying by the factor $\frac{a}{b}$.

The scale on a plan or map is usually given as a ratio

$$\frac{\text{distance on map}}{\text{actual distance}}.$$

This scale is called the representative fraction.

Example:

The map of an area has scale 1:100 000.

If the distance between two towns on the map is 5 cm, what is the actual distance between the towns?

$$\frac{\text{distance on map}}{\text{actual distance}} = \frac{1}{100\,000}$$

$$\Leftrightarrow \frac{\text{actual distance}}{\text{distance on map}} = \frac{100\,000}{1}$$

$$\Leftrightarrow \quad \text{actual distance} \quad = 100\,000 \times \text{distance on map}$$

$$= 100\,000 \times 5\,\text{cm}$$

$$= 500\,000\,\text{cm}$$

$$= 5\,\text{km}$$

Example:

A reproduction of a rectangular painting has length 20 cm. If the actual painting is 1·6 m long and 1 m broad, what breadth is the reproduction?

Let l = length of reproduction

b = breadth of reproduction

L = length of actual painting

B = breadth of actual painting

$\dfrac{b}{l} = \dfrac{B}{L}$ [This order is chosen so that the value to be found is the numerator on the L.H.S. of the equation.]

$\Leftrightarrow \dfrac{b}{20} = \dfrac{1}{1{\cdot}6}$

$\Leftrightarrow b = \dfrac{20}{1{\cdot}6}$

$= 12{\cdot}5$ cm

When ratios as $\dfrac{b}{l}$ and $\dfrac{B}{L}$ above are equal then the variables b, l, B and L are said to be related by direct proportion.

SCALE MODELS

Models are scaled down from actual size and the scale refers to linear measurement. For example if the model is $\dfrac{1}{10}$ of the actual then a model length of 5 cm will represent an actual measurement of 50 cm.

Since area is a square measurement then an area of 5 cm^2 in the model will represent $(5 \times 10 \times 10)$ cm^2 in the actual

Volume or capacity is a cubic measurement so a volume of 5 cm^3 in the model represents $(5 \times 10 \times 10 \times 10)$ cm^3 in the actual. The following example will illustrate the application.

Example:

A model of a cylindrical tank measures 7 cm in length with a base of radius 3 cm. If the scale of the model is $\dfrac{1}{10}$ of the actual tank, find the surface area and volume of the actual tank.

$\left(\text{Take } \pi = \dfrac{22}{7}\right)$

Surface area of model $= (2 \times \pi \times 3^2 + 2 \times \pi \times 3 \times 7)\ \text{cm}^2$

$$= \left(2 \times \tfrac{22}{7} \times 3^2 + 2 \times \tfrac{22}{7} \times 3 \times 7\right)\ \text{cm}^2$$

$$= \tfrac{44}{7}(9 + 21)\ \text{cm}^2$$

$$= \tfrac{1320}{7}\ \text{cm}^2$$

Surface area of actual tank $= \left(\tfrac{1320}{7} \times 100\right)\ \text{cm}^2$

$$= \tfrac{132\,000}{7}\ \text{cm}^2$$

$$= \tfrac{13 \cdot 2}{7}\ \text{m}^2 = 1 \cdot 89\ \text{m}^2 \text{ to 3 s.f.}$$

Volume of model $= \left(\tfrac{22}{7} \times 3^2 \times 7\right)\ \text{cm}^3$

$$= 198\ \text{cm}^3$$

Volume of actual tank $= (198 \times 1000)\ \text{cm}^3$

$$= 198\,000\ \text{cm}^3$$

$$= 198\ \text{litres}$$

DIRECT AND INVERSE PROPORTION

When an increase in one amount brings about a corresponding increase in another then the two quantities are said to be in direct proportion.

e.g. when the radius of a circle is doubled the circumference is doubled, and when the radius is halved the circumference is halved.

When an increase in one amount brings about a corresponding decrease in the other then the two quantities are said to be in inverse proportion.

e.g. when the speed of a car is increased, the time taken to cover a given distance is decreased. If the speed is doubled the time is halved and when the speed is halved the time is doubled.

Example:

In how many days could 10 men do a piece of work which 15 men can do in 20 days?

15 men can do the work in 20 days

1 man can do the work in (20×15) days

10 men can do the work in $\dfrac{20 \times 15}{10}$ days $= 30$ days.

The above example illustrates the unitary method of dealing with proportions in that the amount of time taken by one man is found in the middle step.

All examples in foreign exchange may be dealt with in the above manner.

FOREIGN EXCHANGE

Each country has its own unit of currency and when travelling from one country to another one has to exchange one currency for that of another. The rate of exchange varies from time to time. Listed below are some currencies of other countries and the rate of exchange as it stood at one time during 1990.

Country	Unit of Currency	Number for £1.00
America	Dollar	1.64
Austria	Schilling	19.35
Belgium	Franc	57.82
France	Franc	9.40
Germany (West)	Deutschmark	2.75
Italy	Lira	2066.71
Spain	Peseta	177.94

Example:

How many francs would be given in exchange for £50 to a tourist in France?

Number of francs for £1 $= 9.40$

Number of francs for £50 $= 50 \times 9.40$

$= 470$

Example:

A tourist takes £100 into Germany and there spends 226 deutschmarks. How much sterling will he receive when he leaves?

$$\text{Number of d'marks for £1} = 2.75$$

$$\text{Number of d'marks for £100} = 100 \times 2.75 = 275$$

$$\text{Number of d'marks spent} = 226$$

$$\text{Remainder} = 275 - 226 = 49 \text{ d'marks}$$

$$\text{Number of £'s for 226 d'marks} = 49 \times \frac{1}{2.75} = \frac{49}{2.75}$$

$$= 17.82 \text{ to nearest 1p}$$

If you are not using a calculator then here is the working by long division.

```
         17.818
 275 | 4900.000
       275
       2150
       1925
       2250
       2200
        500
        275
       2250
       2200
         50
```

HOUSE PURCHASE

Money can be borrowed from a Building Society for the purchase of a house. A rate of interest per annum is charged on this loan. It is possible to pay back money to the society to cover the interest charge and reduce the amount of the loan.

Example:

A man borrowed £4000 from a Building Society, the rate of interest being 12% per annum. If he repays £1070 in the first year to cover the interest and reduce the loan, how much did he owe at the beginning of the second year?

How much would he have to repay at the end of the second year to reduce the loan to £2000?

$$\text{Interest due for 1st year} = 12\% \text{ of } £4000$$

$$= £\frac{12 \times 4000}{100}$$

$$= £480$$

$$\text{Amount by which loan is reduced} = £1070 - £480$$

$$= £590$$

$$\text{Amount owed at beginning of 2nd year} = £4000 - £590$$

$$= £3410$$

$$\text{Interest due for 2nd year} = 12\% \text{ of } £3410$$

$$= £\frac{12 \times 3410}{100}$$

$$= £409.20$$

$$\text{Amount necessary to reduce loan to } £2000 = £409.20 + (£3410 - £2000)$$

$$= £409.20 + £1410$$

$$= £1819.20$$

INSURANCE

Insurance Companies agree to pay compensation to a person in event of his having an accident to himself or his property. For this, one has to pay an annual premium. The amount of this premium depends on the amount likely to be paid in compensation.

Example:

A man wishes to insure his house and its contents whose values are £10 000 and £3000 respectively. Calculate the annual premium if the rate is £0.20 per cent for the building and £0.30 per cent for its contents.

$$\text{Premium for building} = £\frac{0 \cdot 20}{100} \times 10\,000 = £20$$

$$\text{Premium for contents} = £\frac{0 \cdot 30}{100} \times 3000 = £9$$

$$\text{Total annual premium} = £20 + £9 = £29$$

Premiums paid for car insurance depend on the capacity of the car, its value, the experience of the driver and the driver's record.

If no claims are made against the insurance company for a year, then the premium is reduced in the following year and this discount is often referred to as the 'no claims bonus'.

Example:

The basic premium for a car insurance is £600 per annum with a 40% discount for 3 years without a claim. How much will the premium be for a driver after 3 years without a claim, but with a 10% excess charge added because of his age?

Discount $= \dfrac{40}{100}$ of £600 = £240

Premium with 40% discount = £600 – £240 = £360

Excess $= \dfrac{10}{100}$ of £360 = £36

Actual Premium $=$ £360 + £36 = £396

A company may never have to pay compensation on an insurance policy if an accident does not occur, but when an assurance policy is taken out then the company will have to pay out money eventually, i.e. when the assured person dies. Such a policy is a whole life policy and the money goes to the assured's dependants.

An alternative assurance is an endowment policy by which as above the sum assured is paid to the dependants in the event of the assured person's death. However such policies are taken out for a certain number of years, e.g. 20 or 30 years, so the assured person may be lucky enough to collect the money himself. The premiums are calculated on the amount assured, the assured's age when the policy is taken out, and the bonus or profits given over and above the total sum of the premiums paid.

INCOME TAX

The amount of money on which tax has to be paid is called taxable income.

Taxable income = total income – allowances

The nature and amount of allowances will be given in any example. The allowances change from year to year after the Budget. The tax year ends on 5th April each year.

Example:

How much tax will a married man pay in a year if he earns £10 000 per annum and is taxed at the basic rate. Give your answer to the nearest £.

Allowances: Single person   £2600

Married man   £3800

Wife's earned income £2500

Basic rate of tax   25%

Taxable income = £10 000 – £3800 = £6200

$$\text{Tax} = £\frac{25}{100} \times \frac{6200}{1} = £1550$$

NUMBER BASES

Since we normally count in tens, we say our calculations are in the base ten. Numbers in the base 10 have place values, e.g. in the number 33 the '3' on the left has a different value from the '3' on the right. The '3' on the left stands for 30, i.e. 3×10, the '3' on the right stands for 3 units, i.e. 3×1.

The number 333 stands for $(3 \times 100) + (3 \times 10) + (3 \times 1)$

i.e. $300 + 30 + 3 = 333$.

Base 10 place values are   Th   H   T   U
10^3 10^2 10^1 1

Since base 10 is used there are ten different digits for each place
i.e. $0, 1, 2, \ldots\ldots\ldots, 9$.

Example:

10^3 10^2 10^1 1
Th   H   T   U
1   2   3   4

The number 1 2 3 4 means $(1 \times 10^3) + (2 \times 10^2) + (3 \times 10^1) + (4 \times 1)$
i.e. $1000 + 200 + 30 + 4 = 1234$

By using the same pattern we may write numbers in any base we choose. For example, for base 2 numbers, i.e. binary numbers, the place values are 2^3 2^2 2^1 1 and since the base is two there are only two possible digits for any place, i.e. 0, 1.

Base two numbers can easily be converted to base 10 by the process used above.

Example:

Convert 1 0 1 1$_2$ (i.e. 1011 in base 2) to base 10 (or denary numbers).

$$2^3 \quad 2^2 \quad 2^1 \quad 1$$
$$1 \quad 0 \quad 1 \quad 1$$

i.e. $(1 \times 2^3) + (0 \times 2^2) + (1^1 \times 2^1) + (1 \times 1)$

$\Leftrightarrow$ 8 + 0 + 2 + 1 = 11

Example:

Convert 2 1 0 2$_3$ to base 10

$$3^3 \quad 3^2 \quad 3^1 \quad 1$$
$$2 \quad 1 \quad 0 \quad 2$$

i.e. $(2 \times 3^3) + (1 \times 3^2) + (0 \times 3^1) + (2 \times 1)$

$\Leftrightarrow$ 54 + 9 + 0 + 2 = 65

Example:

Convert 1 0 1 2 3$_5$ to base 10.

$$5^4 \quad 5^3 \quad 5^2 \quad 5^1 \quad 1$$
$$1 \quad 0 \quad 1 \quad 2 \quad 3$$

i.e. $(1 \times 5^4) + (0 \times 5^3) + (1 \times 5^2) + (2 \times 5^1) + (3 \times 1)$

$\Leftrightarrow$ 625 $\div$ 0 + 25 + 10 + 3 = 663

Numbers in base 10 may be converted to any other base simply by division by the base required.

Example:

Convert 73 to a number in

(a) base 5

```
5 | 73
5 | 14 r3
5 |  2 r4
  |  0 r2
```

$$73 = 2\,4\,3_5$$

(b) base 7

```
7 | 73
7 | 10 r3
7 |  1 r3
  |  0 r1
```

$$73 = 1\,3\,3_7$$

Since $8 = 2^3$ there is a quick way of converting from base 8 to base 2 or vice versa.

Example:

Convert 1 2 5 in base 8 to a binary number.

1	2	5
001	010	101

i.e. convert each digit of base 8 number to a 3 digit binary number.

i.e. $125_8 = 001010101$

$$= 1010101$$

Example:

Convert 1 1 0 1 0 1 1 1 in base 2 to base 8.

011	010	111
3	2	7

i.e. split the binary number into groups of 3 from right to left, then convert each triplet to its decimal equivalent.

i.e. $11010111_2 = 327_8$

ERROR AND TOLERANCE

When measurements are taken then the accuracy is a matter of degree depending on the accuracy of the instruments used, the accuracy of the user and the requirements for which the measure was taken. No measurement then can be exact. The difference between the actual size of what is measured and the measure taken is called the error.

The maximum error in a measurement is half the least unit of measurement. This error is called the absolute error.

Example:

What is the absolute error in the measurement given as 3·04 cm?

The least unit of measurement is found by setting a 1 in the last value position of the measurement given. In the above case, that is in the second decimal place, so the least unit is 0·01 cm.

The absolute error is half of this, i.e. 0·005 cm.

Example:

What is the absolute error in the measurement given as 3·000 cm?

The least unit of measurement is 0·001 cm because the measurement is given correct to the third decimal place as is indicated by the zeros after the decimal point.

$$\text{Absolute error} = \frac{0·001}{2} = 0·0005 \text{ cm}$$

The maximum length of a measured object is equal to the measurement + absolute error. In the first example above the maximum length would be 3·04 + 0·005 = 3·045 cm.

This value is called the upper limit of the measurement.

The minimum length of a measured object is equal to the measurement − absolute error. In the second example above the minimum length would be 3·000 − 0·0005 = 2·9995 cm. This value is called the lower limit of the measurement.

Example:

Find the upper and lower limits of the area of a rectangle whose measurements are given as $1\cdot2$ cm $\times$ $1\cdot0$ cm.

$$\text{Apparent area} = (1\cdot2 \times 1\cdot0)\ \text{cm}^2 \quad = 1\cdot20\ \text{cm}^2$$
$$\text{Maximum area} = (1\cdot25 \times 1\cdot05)\ \text{cm}^2 = 1\cdot3125\ \text{cm}^2$$
$$\text{Minimum area} = (1\cdot15 \times 0\cdot95)\ \text{cm}^2 = 1\cdot0925\ \text{cm}^2$$

Note that the maximum area is the product of the two upper limits.

Note that the minimum area is the product of the two lower limits.

Example:

Find the limits between which the remaining length of a rail must lie if 2.25 cm is to be cut from a length of $5\cdot0$ m.

$$\text{Upper limit} = \text{maximum length of rail} - \text{minimum length of}$$
$$\text{cut section}$$
$$= 5\cdot05 - 2\cdot245 = 2\cdot805\ \text{cm}$$

$$\text{Lower limit} = \text{minimum length of rail} - \text{maximum length of}$$
$$\text{cut section}$$
$$= 4\cdot95 - 2\cdot255 = 2\cdot695\ \text{cm}$$

An absolute error of 1 cm is of no significance when measuring large distances but is disastrous in the components for an alarm clock. The relative importance of the absolute error is given by the relative error, i.e. $\dfrac{\text{absolute error}}{\text{measurement}}$ e.g. the relative error of the measurement of $2\cdot5$ kg is $\dfrac{0\cdot05}{2\cdot5} = \dfrac{5}{250} = \dfrac{1}{50} = 0\cdot02$

Sometimes it is convenient to express the error as a percentage, giving the percentage error, i.e. for the above example the percentage error is $0\cdot02 \times 100 = 2\%$, i.e. percentage error = relative error $\times$ 100.

Notice that the relative error and the percentage error are numbers not units of measurement, but that the absolute error is a measurement in the given units.

Whereas the absolute error is the maximum possible deviation from the true measure, the tolerance is the amount within which a measurement must lie to be acceptable. A given tolerance of $(3{\cdot}5 \pm 0{\cdot}02)$ mm states that for the item to be acceptable it must have an upper limit of $3{\cdot}52$ mm and lower limit of $3{\cdot}48$ mm. Any item within these limits is accepted, any outwith these limits is rejected.

PROBABILITY AND ARRANGEMENTS

Probability is a measure of how likely an event is to occur.

A probability of 1 indicates that an event is certain to occur.
A probability of 0 indicates that an event is certain not to occur.
A probability of $0{\cdot}5$ indicates that an event is just as likely to occur as not.

In general $0 \leqslant \text{prob} \leqslant 1$.

$$\text{Probability} = \frac{\text{number of ways in which the required event occurs}}{\text{number of possible ways the events could occur}}$$

Example:

What is the probability of throwing a 6 with an unbiassed die?

Since the die is unbiassed (not loaded) then each face of the die has an equal probability of turning up. There are 6 possible outcomes, i.e. 1, 2, 3, 4, 5, 6. Only one of these is required.

$$\text{prob} = \frac{1}{6}$$

Example:

What is the probability of throwing a 6 or a 1 with an unbiassed die?

Prob of throwing a 6 $= \dfrac{1}{6}$

Prob of throwing a 1 $= \dfrac{1}{6}$

Prob of throwing a 6 or a 1 $= \dfrac{1}{6} + \dfrac{1}{6}$

$$= \frac{1}{3}$$

When the word 'or' appears in probability examples then the individual probabilities are summed.

Example:

What is the probability of throwing a 6 with an unbiassed die and throwing a 6 on the next turn?

Probability of throwing a 6 on 1st throw $= \dfrac{1}{6}$

Probability of throwing a 6 on 2nd throw $= \dfrac{1}{6}$

Probability of throwing a 6 on 1st and 2nd throws $= \dfrac{1}{6} \times \dfrac{1}{6}$

$$= \dfrac{1}{36}$$

When the word 'and' appears in probability examples then the individual probabilities are multiplied by each other.

Example:

What is the probability of throwing a score greater than 7 but less than 10 in one throw with a pair of unbiassed dice?

Possible outcomes are

$(1, 1)$, $(1, 2)$, $(1, 3)$, $(1, 4)$, $(1, 5)$, $(1, 6)$
$(2, 1)$, $(2, 2)$, $(2, 3)$, $(2, 4)$, $(2, 5)$, $(\underline{2, 6})$
$(3, 1)$, $(3, 2)$, $(3, 3)$, $(3, 4)$, $(\underline{3, 5})$, $(\underline{3, 6})$
$(4, 1)$, $(4, 2)$, $(4, 3)$, $(\underline{4, 4})$, $(\underline{4, 5})$, $(4, 6)$
$(5, 1)$, $(5, 2)$, $(\underline{5, 3})$, $(\underline{5, 4})$, $(5, 5)$, $(5, 6)$
$(6, 1)$, $(\underline{6, 2})$, $(\underline{6, 3})$, $(6, 4)$, $(6, 5)$, $(6, 6)$

From this array of ordered pairs, where the first number in the pair represents the score on one die and the second the score on the second die, 36 possible outcomes appear of which only 9 satisfy the conditions (these are underlined).

So prob $= \dfrac{9}{36} = \dfrac{1}{4}$

Example:

What is the probability that the score in the last example is greater than or equal to 10 but less than or equal to 7?

54

If we know the probability of the event occurring then the probability of its not occurring is found by subtracting the first probability from 1.

i.e. Prob that score is greater than or equal to 10 but less than or equal to 7 is $1 - \frac{1}{4} = \frac{3}{4}$.

An alternative method to the array of ordered pairs is the tree diagram.

Example:

If on the first throw of a die the score is 2 or 3 or 5, what is the probability that the sum of the two scores will be 7 after the second throw?

There are 18 possible outcomes, three of which give the desired total which are underlined.

$$\text{Prob} = \frac{3}{18} = \frac{1}{6}$$

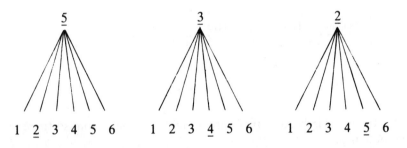

In order to find the probabilities by the use of the array of ordered pairs or by the tree diagram one finds all the possible arrangements or permutations of the data involved. The ordered pairs of the dice scores give all the possible arrangements of 6 different values on each die. Since there were 6 ways for each die to land there were 6 × 6 possible pairs. In general if there are m ways of performing one operation and n ways of performing another then then are $m \times n$ ways of doing both.

Example:

If there are 3 ways of going from A to B and 2 ways of going from B to C.
How many different ways are there of going from A to C?

The diagram illustrates the situation —

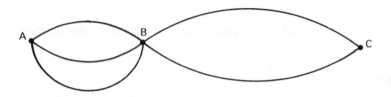

Number of ways from A to B = 3
Number of ways from B to C = 2
Number of ways from A to C = 3 × 2 = 6

Example:

How many different 4 digits numbers can be made from the four digits
2, 8, 5, 7?

How many of these numbers are divisible by 5?

Thousands	Hundreds	Tens	Units

To fill the thousands place there are 4 digits to choose from so there are 4
ways of filling it.

When this place has been filled there are only three digits left from which to
choose, so there are only 3 ways of filling the hundreds place.

The number of ways of filling both these places is then 4 × 3 ways.

There are only two digits left from which to choose to fill the tens place, and
then only one way of filling the units place.

The number of different ways of filling the places is 4 × 3 × 2 × 1 = 24.

To be divisible by 5 the units digit must be 5, so there is only 1 way to fill that position.

There are now only 3 digits to choose from for the tens position, so there are only 3 ways to fill that position.

When these two positions have been filled there are only two digits to choose from to fill the hundreds position so there are only 2 ways of doing that and hence only 1 way to fill the thousands position. In all there are $1 \times 2 \times 3 \times 1 = 6$ ways to have the number divisible by 5.

Using the method of the tree diagram for the above problem we have.

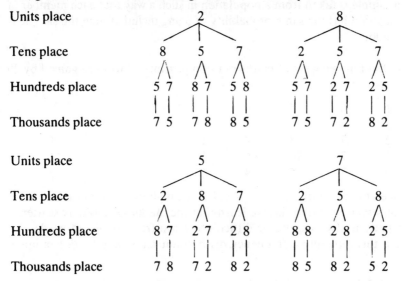

Again giving 24 possibilities.

To be divisible by 5 the tree diagram would be as follows:

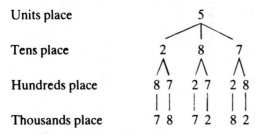

Giving 6 possibilities as before.

STATISTICS

A population comprises all the elements of the set being investigated.

A sample comprises a subset of this population. The population referred to need not refer to persons but simply to a set of observations in the form of numbers called variables, e.g. the heights of 15 year old boys, the number of drivers wearing seat belts, the marks scored by a class of pupils in an arithmetic test, etc.

When a sample is taken from a population in such a way that each member of that population has the same probability of being included then the sample is called random.

Suppose the following set of marks out of a possible of 10 were gained by 25 pupils in a class test.

1	6	5	9	5
3	8	7	4	7
2	7	3	4	6
6	7	10	6	5
9	2	8	4	6

The range of these marks is $10 - 1 = 9$, i.e. the highest observation minus the lowest observation. From this we learn that the marks were widely scattered but the pattern of this scatter is difficult to grasp from the list of marks. To overcome this difficulty a frequency distribution table may be drawn up as follows.

Mark	Tally	Frequency	Mark × Frequency
1	I	1	1
2	I I	2	4
3	I I	2	6
4	I I I	3	12
5	I I I	3	15
6	⊦⊦⊦⊦	5	30
7	I I I I	4	28
8	I I	2	16
9	I I	2	18
10	I	1	10
		25	140

Under the heading 'Mark' are listed 10 classes. In each class is placed all the different marks in the range of the variable.

Under the heading 'Tally' a vertical line is placed for each time the variable in any class occurs in the list of marks. The best way to do this is to go through the list and enter a vertical line in the appropriate class. For example if the list is scanned vertically then the first vertical line will go in class 1, the second in class 3, the third in class 2 and so on. When four tally lines have been entered then the fifth one is a slanted line through the other four as in class 6.

Under 'Frequency' the number of tally lines is entered.

Under 'Mark × Frequency' the product of the mark and frequency in each class is entered. The last two columns in the table have been totalled because from them the mean of the distribution is calculated.

The mean is what is often referred to as the average but as shall be seen later it is only one of the so called averages.

$$\text{Mean} = \frac{(\text{Mark} \times \text{Frequency}) \text{ total}}{\text{Frequency total}}$$

$$= \frac{140}{25} = 5 \cdot 6 = 6 \text{ to 1 s.f.}$$

Notice that the frequency total gives a check that all 25 observations in the list have been accounted for.

Another average is the mode. The mode is the observation which has the highest frequency, i.e. 6 is the mode in this example.

The median is yet another average. The median is the middle observation after they have been arranged in order. The frequency table has arranged the marks in order so the middle mark is the 13th since this would leave 12 marks above and 12 marks below. By counting down the frequency column the 13th mark lies in class 6. So 6 is the median of this distribution.

Here the mean = median = mode = 6 which indicates that the marks are fairly evenly distributed. It is not usually the case that the three averages are equal as shall be seen later.

A more graphic appreciation of the distribution may be gained by a visual presentation in the form of a histogram or a frequency polygon.

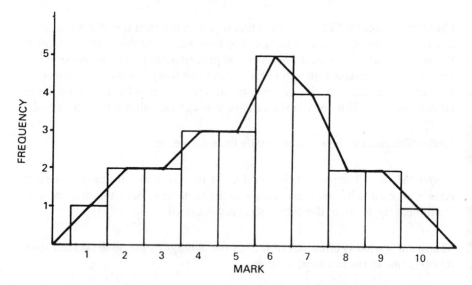

The vertical axis of a histogram is the frequency axis evenly calibrated up to the modal frequency, i.e. the number of times the mode 6 occurred. The horizontal axis is named after the type of observations made, calibrated evenly to accommodate the number of classes used.

There are no gaps between the rectangles for each class but half a rectangle width is left before the first class and after the last class.

The height of each rectangle is reckoned from the frequency of the class it represents.

A frequency polygon has been superimposed on the histogram by joining the mid-points of the tops of each rectangle with straight lines.

Where adjacent classes have the same frequency the lines merge into the tops of the rectangles. Notice where the frequency polygon begins and ends. The observations in this example were found by counting, so such variables are said to be discrete.

If the values of the variables are found by measurement then the variables are said to be continuous.

60

From the frequency table such questions as "what percentage of pupils scored 3 or less?" may be answered.

If the frequencies of those who scored 1, 2, 3 are totalled it is found that 5 scored 3 or less, i.e. 5 pupils out of 25 giving $\frac{5}{25} \times 100\% = 20\%$. When $\frac{5}{25}$ is expressed as a decimal we refer to this value as the relative frequency. For example the relative frequency of the mark of 8 is $\frac{2}{25}$ i.e. 0·08. The total of the relative frequencies of all classes is always 1.

GROUPED FREQUENCY DISTRIBUTION TABLES

Where there are too many observations to allow one class for each they are grouped in class intervals. There should be between 8 and 12 classes for convenience and a fair degree of accuracy.

Example:

Draw a cumulative frequency curve (ogive) to represent the distribution of heights, to the nearest mm, of experimental plants.

Find also the mean height and the modal class.

Heights to nearest mm	53 to 55	56 to 58	59 to 61	62 to 64	65 to 67	68 to 70	71 to 73	74 to 76	77 to 79
Frequency	1	2	4	9	10	8	3	2	1

The class interval of the first class is 3 mm, i.e. 53 to 55 for it contains those which measured 53 mm or 54 mm or 55 mm.

The class limits of the second class, for example, are 56, which is the lower class limit, and 58 which is the upper class limit.

Since the mesurements are to the nearest mm then a plant which measures 67·3 mm will be placed in the class 65–67 mm. In fact any plant up to 67·5 mm which is called the upper class boundary will go into the same class. Plants greater than 67·5 mm will go into the next class 68–70 mm. 67·5 is the lower class boundary for the class 68–70 mm.

The horizontal table in the question is really the first two columns of the grouped frequency distribution table but is printed this way to save space.

Height	Frequency	Mid Value	Frequency × Mid Value
53 – 55	1	54	54
56 – 58	2	57	114
59 – 61	4	60	240
62 – 64	9	63	567
65 – 67	10	66	660
68 – 70	8	69	552
71 – 73	3	72	216
74 – 76	2	75	150
77 – 79	1	78	78
	40		2631

$$\text{Mean} = \frac{2631}{40} = 65.7 = 66 \text{ to nearest mm.}$$

Notice that the mid-value of each class is required to find a corresponding column to the 'Mark × Frequency of the first example.

PIE CHART

Example:

720 cars passing a certain point were tabulated according to their colour. 180 were blue, 120 were red, 120 were white, 60 were green, 20 were black, the remainder were combinations of two tones and other colours. Draw a pie chart to represent this distribution of colours.

The ratio of each colour over the total number is used as a fraction of the area of a circle in the form of a sector. The angle subtended at the centre of the circle by the sector is found as follows.

Sector representing blue cars subtends angle $\left(\frac{180}{720} \times 360\right)^{\circ} = 90°$

Sector representing red cars subtends angle $\left(\frac{120}{720} \times 360\right)^{\circ} = 60°$

Sector representing white cars subtends angle $\left(\frac{120}{720} \times 360\right)^{\circ} = 60^{\circ}$

Sector representing green cars subtends angle $\left(\frac{60}{720} \times 360\right)^{\circ} = 30^{\circ}$

Sector representing black cars subtends angle $\left(\frac{20}{720} \times 360\right)^{\circ} = 10^{\circ}$

Sector representing others   subtends angle $360^{\circ} - (90 + 60 + 60 + 30 + 10)^{\circ}$

$$360^{\circ} - 250^{\circ}$$

$$= 110^{\circ}$$

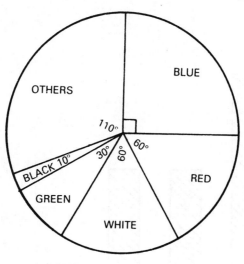

BAR GRAPH

The information from the previous example could be represented on a bar graph as follows, where the heights of the bars indicate the frequency of each colour.

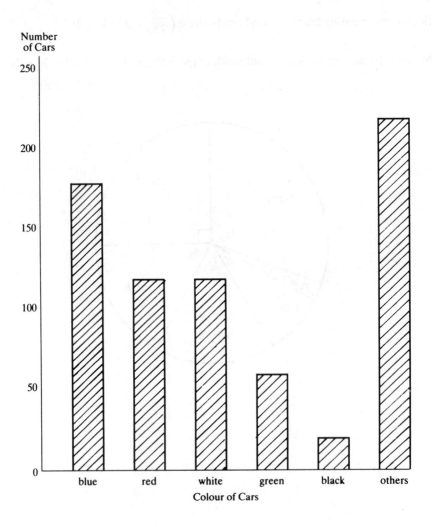

LINE GRAPH

The line graph relates one variable with another, e.g. time and distance or as the diagram shows time and temperature from midnight till 0200 where the temperature was taken every half hour. By joining the readings plotted every half hour one is interpolating by following the trend, i.e. assuming that, e.g. Mr. R.I.P.'s temperature did not rise and fall several times between midnight and 0030.

Notice the zig-zag line at the foot of the temperature axis which indicates that the section from 0° to 34° is not to scale.

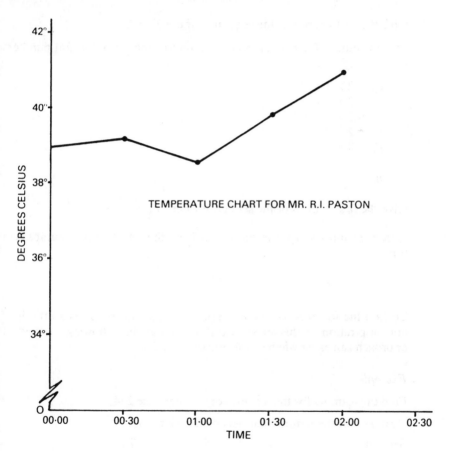

TEMPERATURE CHART FOR MR. R.I. PASTON

SEQUENCES n^{th} Terms

Numbers arranged in order according to some rule are called sequences, e.g.

(a) 2, 4, 6, 8, ...

The rule is add 2 to each number (term) to get the next term.

We could name the terms T_1, T_2, T_3 and in the above sequence $T_1 = 2$, $T_2 = 4$, $T_3 = 6$, etc.

The nth term of the sequence is denoted by T_n so that $T_n + 2 = T_{n+1}$, i.e. for example $T_3 + 2 = T_4$ $(6 + 2 = 8)$.

(b) Give the first 4 terms of the sequence where $T_n = 2n$.

By substitution for n when n is a member of the set of natural numbers $\{1, 2, 3, 4, 5, ...\}$

$$T_1 = 2 \times 1 = 2$$
$$T_2 = 2 \times 2 = 4$$
$$T_3 = 2 \times 3 = 6$$
$$T_4 = 2 \times 4 = 8$$
$$T_n = 2 \times n = 2n$$

Example:

Give the first 3 terms of the sequence where $T_n = \dfrac{n^3}{2} + 1$.

Here we simply substitute the values from the set of natural numbers in turn.

$$T_1 = \frac{1}{2} + 1 = \frac{3}{2}, \ T_2 = \frac{8}{2} + 1 = \underline{5}, \ T_3 = \frac{27}{2} + 1 = \underline{14\tfrac{1}{2}}$$

To find the formula for the nth term of a sequence requires a little luck and inspiration at this stage of arithmetic but the following method of approach can assist when simple inspection fails.

Example:

Find the formula for the nth term of the sequence 2, 4, 6, 8, ... T_n

First pair off the natural numbers with each term.

Sequence	2	4	6	8	..........T_n
Natural Numbers	1	2	3	4	.........n

Now examine the pairings from the natural numbers to the sequence to see if you can multiply by any factor to give the sequence. Here we multiply by 2, so $T_n = 2n$

| Sequence | 2 | 4 | 6 | 8 | .... | T_n |
| 2 × Natural Numbers | 2 | 4 | 6 | 8 | .... | $2n$ |

Example:

Find the formula for the nth term of the sequence 1, 3, 5, 7, 9 ...., T_n

| Sequence | 1 | 3 | 5 | 7 | 9 | .... | T_n |
| Natural Numbers | 1 | 2 | 3 | 4 | 5 | .... | n |

There is no factor here by which to multiply but by multiplying by 2 the two sequences get nearer.

| Sequence | 1 | 3 | 5 | 7 | 9 | .... | T_n |
| 2 × Natural Numbers | 2 | 4 | 6 | 8 | 10 | .... | $2n$ |

It now becomes obvious that we need only subtract 1 from each term in the lower line to give the terms of the sequence.

| Sequence | | 1 | 3 | 5 | 7 | 9 | T_n |
| (2 × Natural Numbers) – 1 | 2 – 1 | 4 – 1 | 6 – 1 | 8 – 1 | 10 – 1 | $2n – 1$ |

The nth term then is $2n – 1$.

Example:

Find the formula for the nth term of the sequence 5, 8, 11, 14, ... T_n

| Sequence | 5 | 8 | 11 | 14 | .... | T_n |
| Natural Numbers | 1 | 2 | 3 | 4 | .... | n |

Multiplying by 2 would not bring us much nearer, so try multiplying by 3.

| Sequence | 5 | 8 | 11 | 14 | .... | T_n |
| 3 × Natural Numbers | 3 | 6 | 9 | 12 | .... | $3n$ |

It is now clear that we need only add 2 to match the pairs.

Sequence		5	8	11	14	....	T_n
3 × Natural Numbers + 2		3 + 2	6 + 2	9 + 2	12 + 2	....	$3n + 2$

The nth term then is $3n + 2$

Example:

Find the formula for the nth term of the sequence 5, 8, 13, 20, ..., T_n

Sequence	5	8	13	20	....	T_n
Natural Numbers	1	2	3	4	....	n

Multiplying by 2, 3, 4 seems no use so try squaring the natural numbers.

Sequence	5	8	13	20	....	T_n
(Natural Numbers)^2	1	4	9	16	....	n^2

Now add 4.

Sequence		1	8	13	20	....	T_n
(Natural Numbers)^2 + 4	1 + 4	4 + 4	9 + 4	16 + 4	....	$n^2 + 4$

From these examples it should be seen that the aim is to find a factor such that the difference between the pairs in each row is the same. Failing this try squaring or even cubing the natural numbers till the difference between the pairs in each row is the same. Having achieved this we then add or subtract the difference between the pairs so that they match.

Watch out for familiar sequences such as

$$2, 3, 5, 7, 11, ...$$

i.e. the sequence of prime numbers. Since no rule has yet been found to give T_n of the prime numbers it is debatable whether or not this is in fact a sequence.

1, 1, 2, 3, 5, 8, 13 is the Fibonacci sequence. Here each term is the sum of the two preceding terms, e.g. $5 = (2 + 3)$, $8 = (3 + 5)$, etc.

Another common sequence is that of the triangular numbers 1, 3, 6, 10, 15, ... where $T_n = \dfrac{n(n + 1)}{2}$

Look at the shape of the following patterns and count the dots in each.

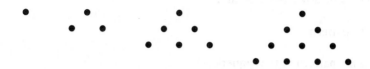

Patterns like this give rise to such questions as "How many match sticks will be required to make a 5 × 5 square on the following pattern where each side of the small squares has one match?"

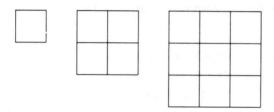

By examination of the design of the pattern we see that it consists simply of rows and columns of matches.

In the first   there are 2 rows + 2 columns
In the second there are 3 rows + 3 columns
In the third   there are 4 rows + 4 columns so by deduction
In the fifth   there are 6 rows + 6 columns
In the nth there are $(n + 1) + (n + 1)$ columns

In each row and column there will be 5 matches, so the total number of matches for a 5 × 5 square will be (6×5) for the rows and (6×5) for the columns, i.e. 60 matches.

Example:

How many dots will there be in the

(a) 12th pattern

(b) the nth pattern of the sequence

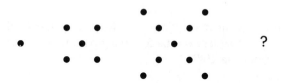

(a) Each pattern after the first comprises 4 arms of dots and one dot in the centre.

The 1st   pattern has $(4 \times 0) + 1 = 1$ dot
The 2nd pattern has $(4 \times 1) + 1 = 5$ dots
The 3rd   pattrn has $(4 \times 2) + 1 = 9$ dots
The 12th pattern has $(4 \times 11) + 1 = 45$ dots

(b) The nth pattern has $(4 \times [n-1]) + 1 = (4n-4) + 1$
$\qquad\qquad = 4n - 3$ dots

FLOW CHARTS

Computers are used to perform routine tasks quickly and accurately. To do this they must be given data on which to work and instructions as to how the work has to be done. These instructions are given to the computer in a coded form.

The instructions are written by the computer programmer using a programming language, e.g. **BASIC**. The task to be performed must first be broken into simple steps, for there are only a limited number of operations which the computer can perform. These steps are planned and put in diagram form called a flow chart.

70

A flow chart has instructions entered in a rectangular box, and questions which are entered in a diamond shaped box. The boxes are linked by lines which have arrows showing where the next step is to be found. There may be more than one way into any box but only one way out. An exception to this rule is the question box which usually has two ways out, but this is because the box may contain questions which have only two possible answers 'yes' or 'no'. The way out will depend on the answer given to the question. The following flow chart will illustrate these points.

The problem is to write a program flow chart which will select all the even numbers from the set A = (1, 2, 3, 4, 5, 6, 7, 8, 9, 10). A rounded shape will indicate where the chart starts and ends.

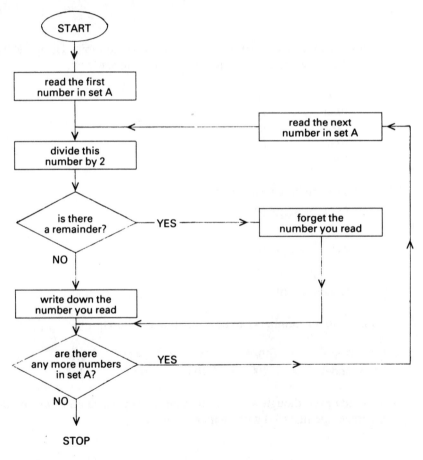

The results to be written down should be 2, 4, 6, 8, 10.

INDEX NUMBERS

Index numbers are used to compare one year's figures against those for other years.

For example, we might want to compare the cost of living now with that of the last 3 years.

The year we wish to compare others with is called the base year. The figures for other years are expressed as percentages of this.

Example:

The cost of food from 1980 to 1983 is given in the table. Using 1980 as the base year express the cost for the other years in index form.

Year	Cost
1980	£50
1981	£52
1982	£55
1983	£56

Since 1980 is the base year we let

£50 represents 100,

so

£52 represents 104

£55 represents 110

£56 represents 112

This set of index numbers can be tabulated as follows:

Year	1980	1981	1982	1983
Index	100	104	110	112

Notice that even though we are using a percentage calculation we do not need the percentage sign (%) with an index number.

AN INVESTIGATION

How many squares are there on a chess board?

Even if we know or are told the correct number of squares there would be no credit given for simply writing the number. The question asked should be treated as a guide to a line of investigation that will lead to finding the correct answer as follows:

1. Say what you are trying to do.

2. Say how you will go about it.

3. Start with the simplest situation.

4. Draw some diagrams.

5. Make a table of your results.

6. Look for a pattern or rule in the results.

7. Check your pattern or rule by predicting the next set of results.

8. Say what your rule or pattern is.

9. Answer the original question.

10. Generalise your rule.

I am asked to find how many squares there are on a chess board. A chess board is made up of 64 small squares but there are larger squares which can be found by grouping the small squares together. I will call the small squares unit squares or 1×1 squares. I will start by examining a simpler set of 'chess boards' of sizes 1×1, 2×2, 3×3, 4×4, etc., draw some diagrams and make a table of my results.

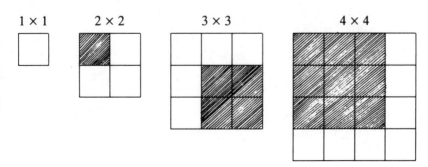

1×1 2×2 3×3 4×4

Size of Board	Number of squares of size			
	1×1	2×2	3×3	4×4
1×1	1			
2×2	4	1		
3×3	9	4	1	
4×4	16	9	4	1

When the first three diagrams were drawn and the results entered into the table I noticed a pattern of square numbers. I predicted the results of a 4×4 board then drew it out to check that the result was correct. The table was written again to show the pattern more clearly.

Size of Board	Number of squares of size			
	1×1	2×2	3×3	4×4
1×1	1^2			
2×2	2^2	1^2		
3×3	3^2	2^2	1^2	
4×4	4^2	3^2	2^2	1^2

The result for the 8×8 chess board can now be written as

$$8^2 + 7^2 + 6^2 + 5^2 + 4^2 + 3^2 + 2^2 + 1^2 = 204 \text{ squares.}$$

In general for any size of board, $n \times n$, the total number of squares is

$$n^2 + (n-1)^2 + (n-2)^2 + (n-3)^2 + \dots\dots + 3^2 + 2^2 + 1^2$$

74

POINTS

A point marks a position in space.

A capital letter is used to name a point.

Below are the points A and B.

Since we cannot measure a point it is said to have no dimensions.

A   B
•   •

LINES

A line joins points.

Two capital letters are used to name a line.

Below is the line segment AB which joins the point A to point B.

The straight line is the shortest distance between two points on the plane.

Since we can measure only the length of a line it is said to have one dimension — its length.

A _____ B

PARALLEL LINES

When two straight lines are always the same distance apart they are said to be parallel to each other.

Below AB is parallel to CD.

A _____→_____ B

C _____→_____ D

The arrows on the lines show that they are parallel lines.

HORIZONTAL LINES

The line where the sky seems to meet the sea is called the horizon. A line which is parallel to the horizon is called a horizontal line. A horizontal line is usually drawn across the page as is shown by AB below.

A _____ B

VERTICAL LINES

A line which shows the path of a falling object is called a vertical line.
The path of a ball which is dropped from your hand is a vertical line.
A vertical line is usually drawn down the page as is shown below.

PERPENDICULAR LINES

A horizontal line is perpendicular to a vertical line.
A horizontal line meets a vertical line at right angles.
Below AB is perpendicular to XY.

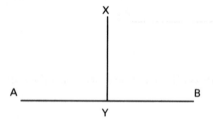

Two lines which meet at right angles are perpendicular even though they are not horizontal and vertical.

Below AB is perpendicular to XY.

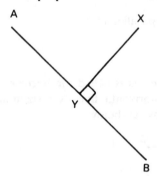

BISECTING LINES

When one line cuts another in half the first line is said to bisect the second.

Below the line AB bisects the line XY at M.

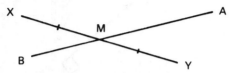

XM = YM and M is called the mid-point of XY.

AB does not have to be perpendicular to XY in order to bisect it.

ANGLES

When the minute hand goes round the clock face and back to where it started it has made a *full turn* or one *revolution*. The amount of turning is measured in degrees. A full turn has 360 degrees (360°).

In half an hour the minute hand will have made a *half turn* or 180°.

In a quarter of an hour the minute hand will have made a *quarter turn* or 90° or 1 right angle.

A right angle is shown below.

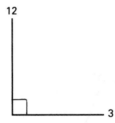

The mark ⌐ is used to show that an angle is right.

ACUTE ANGLES

When the hand of a clock has turned through less than 90° it is said to have turned through an acute angle.

The examples below show the hand has turned through acute angles.

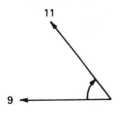

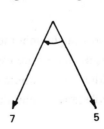

RIGHT ANGLES

The examples below show the hand has turned through a right angle.

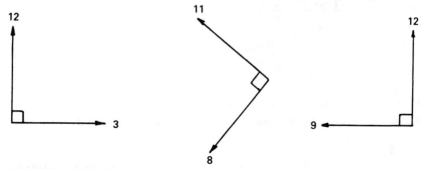

OBTUSE ANGLES

When the hand of a clock has turned through more than a right angle but less than a half turn it is said to have turned through an obtuse angle.

The examples below show that the hands have turned through obtuse angles.

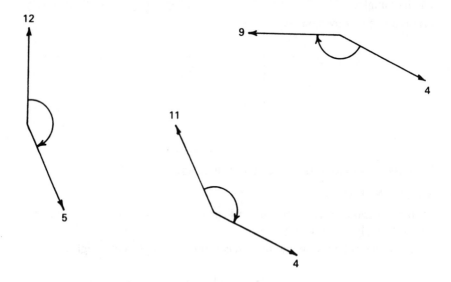

When two straight lines meet they make an angle.

Three capital letters are used to name an angle.

The middle letter is where the lines meet.

The middle letter names the vertex of the angle.

The acute angle ABC is shown below.

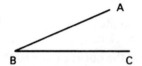

AB is an arm of the angle.
BC is the other arm of the angle.
B is the vertex of the angle.

Angle ABC can be written as A$\hat{B}$C or $\angle$ ABC.

It does not matter if the angle is named A$\hat{B}$C or C$\hat{B}$A as long as the vertex letter is the middle letter.

The right angle XYZ is shown below.

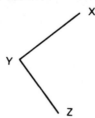

The obtuse angle PQR is shown below.

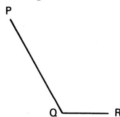

A *protractor* is used to measure the size of an angle.

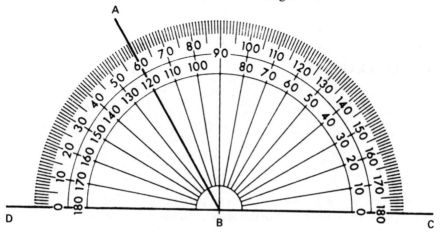

79

In the diagram on page 79 the protractor shows that angle ABC is 120° and that angle ABD is 60°.

Notice that the zero on the arm of angle ABC is on the inside scale so the size of the angle ABC is read from the inside scale, i.e. 120°.

Note that the zero on the arm of angle ABD is on the outside scale so the size of the angle ABD is read from the outside scale, i.e. 60°.

SUPPLEMENTARY ANGLES

When the sum of two angles is 180° the angles are said to be supplementary.

In the diagram below AX̂B is the supplement of AX̂C.

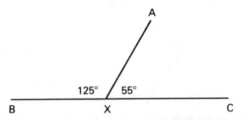

COMPLEMENTARY ANGLES

When the sum of two angles is 90° the angles are said to be complementary.

In the diagram below AB̂X is the complement of XB̂C.

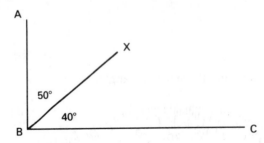

COMPASS BEARINGS

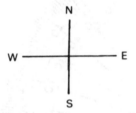

The diagram above shows the four compass points — North, South, East, West. The north-south line is perpendicular to the east-west line.

The compass directions between N, S, E and W are shown in the diagram below.

They are north-east, south-east, south-west and north-west.

The angle between the north line and the north-east line is 45°.

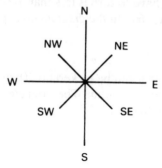

In the diagram below ship A is due north of ship B, ship C is due east of ship B, ship D is north-west of ship B. Ship B is due south of ship A, ship B is due west of ship C, ship B is south-east of ship D.

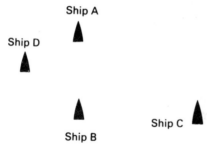

THREE-FIGURE BEARINGS

To find the bearing of a ship from any spot we must first look north then turn to the right to face the ship. The angle through which we turn gives the bearing of the ship. In the diagram below, suppose we are standing at C and wish to know the bearing of ship A and ship B.

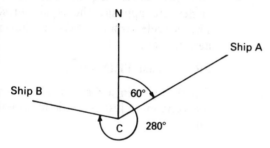

By looking north and turning to look at ship A we turn through 60°. The bearing of ship A is 060°.

Ship B is on a bearing of 280°.

Notice that if the number of degrees we have to turn is less than 100 then we put a zero first as in the bearing of ship A, 060°, in the diagram on page 81.

PLANE FIGURES

Plane or flat figures are not solid shapes that can be picked up. They are said to have only two dimensions, length and breadth. The triangle, square, rectangle and circle are examples of plane figures.

TRIANGLES

Equilateral triangles have three sides all of the same length and three angles each measuring 60°. Three capital letters, in any order, are used to name a triangle. The equilateral triangle ABC is shown here.

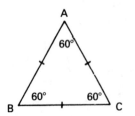

Each side of the triangle is named by two capital letters.

AB = BC = AC and so all have the same mark on them in the diagram.

$A\hat{B}C = A\hat{C}B = B\hat{A}C = 60°$.

Notice that when all three angles of the triangle are added together the sum is 180°. This is true for all triangles and we say that the sum of the angles of a triangle is 180° or two right angles.

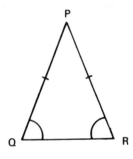

Isosceles triangles have two sides equal and two angles equal. The equal angles are opposite the equal sides. The isosceles triangle PQR is drawn here for you.

$PR = PQ$ and $P\hat{R}Q = P\hat{Q}R$.

Equal angles in a diagram are given the same mark just as we do for equal sides.

Right-angled triangles have one angle which is equal to 90°.

The side opposite the right angle is called the *hypotenuse*.

In this right-angled triangle AC is the hypotenuse.

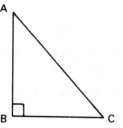

The hypotenuse is the longest side of a right-angled triangle.

The longest side of a triangle is always opposite the biggest angle and the shortest side is always opposite the smallest angle.

The corners of a triangle are called the vertices since each corner is the vertex of an angle.

A **scalene triangle** is one where all three angles are of different size which means that all three sides will be of different size.

An **acute-angled triangle** is one where all three angles are acute.

An **obtuse-angled triangle** is one where one of the angles is an obtuse angle.

Since the sum of the angles of a triangle is 180° we need to be told the sizes of only two angles in order to find the size of the third one. For example, if one angle is 60° and the other is 30° then their sum is 90° so the third angle must be 90°, which means that the triangle is a right-angled one.

THE SQUARE

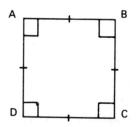

A square has four sides all of the same length and four angles each of 90°.

The opposite sides of a square are parallel to each other.

The name of the square above is ABCD. The name of a plane figure is read clockwise or anticlockwise (DCBA). It does not matter at which vertex we start as long as we keep reading the same way round, e.g. CBAD or BADC or CDAB, etc.

The lines joining the opposite vertices of a square are called *diagonals*.

A square has two diagonals AC and BD as shown in this figure.

The diagonals of a square are equal to each other, i.e. AC = BD.

The diagonals of a square bisect each other.

The diagonals of a square are perpendicular to each other.

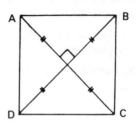

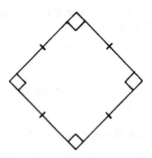

This figure is also a square because it has all the features mentioned above.

THE RECTANGLE

A rectangle has four sides. The opposite sides are parallel and equal to each other.

The four angles of the rectangle are right angles. ABCD is a rectangle.

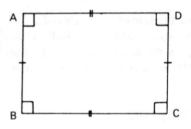

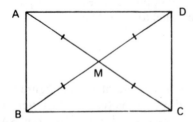

In this rectangle ABCD the diagonals are shown.

The diagonals of a rectangle are equal, AC = BD.

The diagonals of a rectangle bisect each other,
AM = MC = BM = MD.

The sum of the angles of the square and the rectangle are easily seen to be four right angles or 360°.

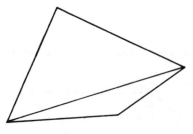

The sum of the angles of any plane figure with four sides is 360°.

A diagonal of any plane four-sided figure cuts the figure into two triangles and since the sum of the angles of a triangle is 180° the sum for the two triangles is 360°.

THE CIRCLE 1

This diagram shows the *circumference* of the circle with *centre* O.

The point O is the same distance from every point on the circumference.

This distance is called the *radius* of the circle.

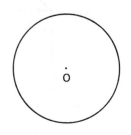

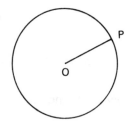

This diagram shows the circle with centre O and a radius OP.

This diagram shows a circle with centre O and a *diameter* AB.

A diameter is twice the length of the radius.

The centre O is the mid-point of the diameter.

The small letter 'r' is used to stand for the radius and the small letter 'd' for the diameter.

d = 2r says that the diameter is two times the radius.

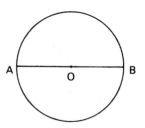

SOLID SHAPES OR 3D SHAPES

Solid shapes are said to have three dimensions — length, breadth and height.

The Cube

The cube has   6 faces
8 vertices
12 edges

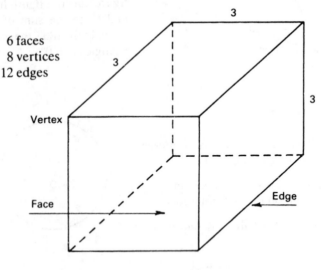

If the length of one edge of the cube is 3 units then the length of every other edge is 3 units.

Notice that in the diagram above the 'hidden' edges are marked by broken lines.

In the diagram below AC is called a *face diagonal* and HC is called a *space diagonal*.

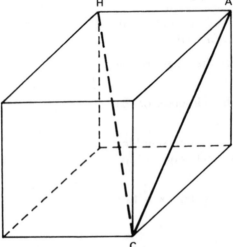

The Cuboid

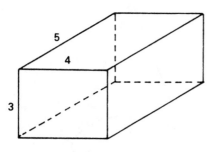

The cuboid has   6 faces
                           8 vertices
                           12 edges

Four of the faces of a cuboid will be rectangles; the other two may be either squares or rectangles.

The diagram shows a 3 by 4 by 5 cuboid or a $3 \times 4 \times 5$ cuboid.

There are four edges of 3 units.

There are four edges of 4 units.

There are four edges of 5 units.

As in the cube there are face diagonals and space diagonals.

The space diagonals are all the same size as each other, but there are three different sizes of face diagonals.

The lengths of the face and space diagonals are both found by using the Theorem of Pythagoras which is explained later in the text.

The Pyramid

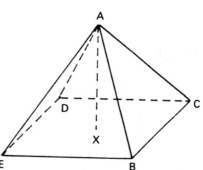

The pyramid has   5 faces
                       5 vertices
                       8 edges

BCDE is called the base of the pyramid.

The base of a pyramid may be a rectangle or a square.

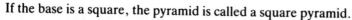

If the base is a square, the pyramid is called a square pyramid.

AX is the height of the pyramid. AX is perpendicular to the base.

The pyramid has four triangular faces.

Other pyramids may be drawn where the base is a parallelogram or a rhombus, etc.

Notice that in drawing a pyramid with a rectangular base the angles of the base do not look like right angles because we are drawing a 3D figure on a 2D surface. Look back at the cube and cuboid and you will notice the same thing has happened there.

The Cone

The cone has   2 faces
                   1 vertex
                   1 edge

The base of the cone is a circle.

The base of the cone is a face.

The rest of the cone is a face but it is a curved face.

A is the vertex of the cone.

AO is the height of the cone.

OP is the radius of the circular base.

AP is the *slant height* of the cone.

When AO is perpendicular to the base we have a *right circular cone* and AOP is a right-angled triangle.

The base of the cone in the diagram does not look like a circle because we are drawing a 3D figure on a 2D surface.

The Cylinder

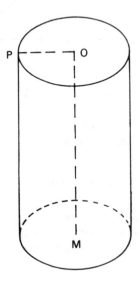

The cylinder has   3 faces
                   0 vertices
                   2 edges.

Two of the faces of the cylinder are circles, one face is curved.

OP is the radius of the circular face, or the radius of the cylinder.

OM is the height of the cylinder.

When there is a top and bottom to the cylinder it is called a closed cylinder.

When there is no top or bottom it is called an open cylinder. A piece of pipe is an open cylinder.

The Sphere

The sphere has only one curved surface.

A snooker ball is a sphere.

OP is the radius of the sphere.

Every point on the surface of the sphere is the same distance from O, the centre of the sphere.

The Earth is considered as a sphere with N the North Pole and S the South Pole and the circle with radius OP the Equator.

The sphere is the solid with the greatest volume for a given surface area.

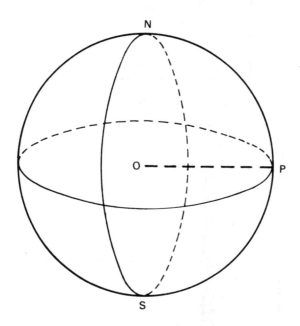

89

DRAWING PARALLEL LINES

A set-square and a ruler can be used to draw parallel lines.

The following method can be used to draw parallel lines 3 cm apart.

First draw a straight line with a ruler.

Place an edge of the set-square (not the hypotenuse) on the line.

Place the ruler against the set-square.

Slide the set-square down 3 cm.

Draw a line using the edge of the set-square that lay on the first line.

The diagram below illustrates the method.

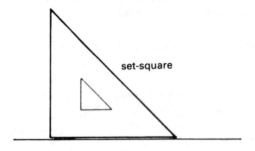

set-square

NOTE: The set-square is not drawn to scale.

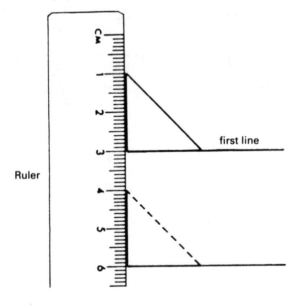

Ruler

first line

DRAWING TRIANGLES

To draw triangles of a given size we need a ruler, compass and protractor.

1. Three sides given, e.g. 7 cm, 5 cm and 4 cm.
   We need a ruler and a compass.
   First draw a line 7 cm long.
   Name the line AB.

A   B

Set the compass with radius 5 cm.
Put the point of the compass at B.
Draw an arc (part of a circle's circumference).

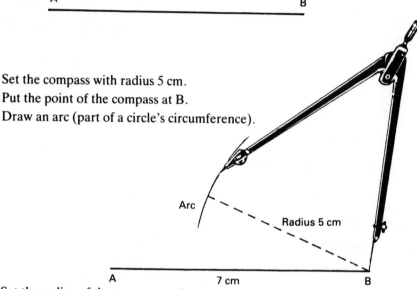

Set the radius of the compass at 4 cm.

Put the point of the compass at A.

Draw an arc to cut the first one and name the point where the arcs cross C.

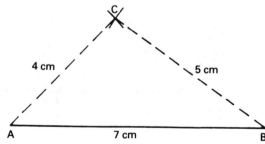

Now join A to C and B to C.

91

2. Two sides and the angle between them given, e.g. 7 cm, 5 cm and 60°.

We need a ruler and a protractor.

First draw a line 7 cm long.

Name the line AB.

With the protractor, using B as the vertex, draw an angle ABD of 60°.

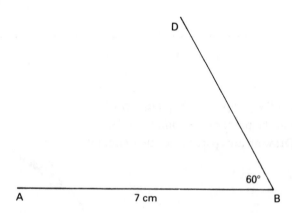

Mark a point on the line BD, 5 cm from B.

Name the point C.

Join A to C.

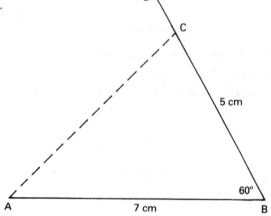

3.   Two angles and a side given, e.g. 60°, 40°, 7 cm.

We need a ruler and protractor.

First draw a line 7 cm long.

Name the line AB.

With the protractor, using B as the vertex, draw an angle of 60°.

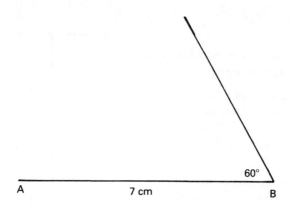

With the protractor, using A as the vertex, draw an angle of 40°.

Where the arm of the 60° angle cuts the arm of the 40° angle is the third vertex of the triangle.

If the arms are not long enough to cut each other then use your ruler to draw them long enough to cross.

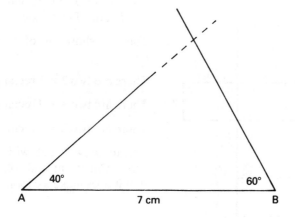

NETS OF SOLIDS

If a solid were made of cardboard and then opened out flat we would have a shape called a net of the solid.

Solids can be opened out flat in different ways and so can have more than one shape of net.

Net of a Cube

The net has six squares which would make the six faces of the cube.

If the opposite faces of a die add up to seven and the net in the diagram were the net of the die, what numbers would be on faces A, B, C and D when face X is 1 and face Y is 6?

Try to draw other nets of the cube on squared cardboard or paper, cut them out and fold them up to check that they do make cubes.

X	A	Y
	B	
	C	
	D	

Net of a Cuboid

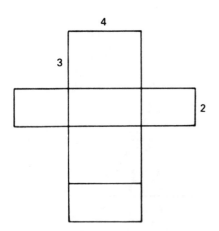

The net of a cuboid has six parts or three pairs of rectangles.

The net shown is of a 2 × 3 × 4 cuboid.

There are two 2 × 3 rectangles.

There are two 3 × 4 rectangles.

There are two 2 × 4 rectangles.

Try to draw a net with two square faces. Cut it out and fold it to check that it does make a cuboid.

94

Net of a Square Pyramid

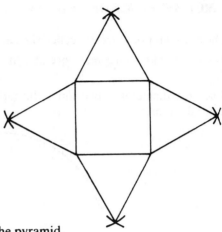

First draw a square for the base of the pyramid.

Draw the triangles on each side of the square using a compass to first draw the arcs of a circle as shown earlier in the text when drawing triangles.

The same size of radius is used for all eight arcs.

PERIMETER

The perimeter of a plane figure is the total distance around its edges.

The perimeter of the rectangle shown is
4 cm + 3 cm + 4 cm + 3 cm = 14 cm.

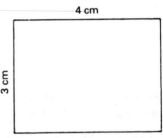

Since the opposite edges of a rectangle are the same length we could say that the *p*erimeter is 2 × *l*ength + 2 × *b*readth or in short form

$$P = 2l + 2b$$

$P = 2l + 2b$ is a formula for finding the perimeter of a rectangle.

The perimeter of a square of side 5 cm is 20 cm since all the sides are the same length. There are four sides the same length in a square so the formula for the perimeter of a square is $P = 4l$.

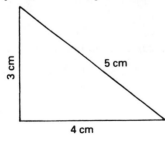

To find the perimeter of a triangle we add the lengths of the three sides. For example, the perimeter of the triangle here is 3 cm + 4 cm + 5 cm = 12 cm.

If the edges are measured in cm then the perimeter is given in cm.

CIRCUMFERENCE OF A CIRCLE

The perimeter of a circle is called the circumference.

The length of the circumference of a circle is roughly three times its diameter, d.

Since the diameter is two times the radius the circumference is roughly six times the radius, r.

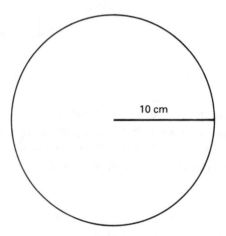

10 cm

In the circle above whose radius is 10 cm (not drawn to scale) the circumference is roughly $6 \times 10 = 60$ cm.

Since the diameter is 20 cm the circumference is roughly $3 \times 20 = 60$ cm.

The exact length of the circumference is a little more than 60 cm.

The circumference is given by the formula $C = \pi d$ where π is taken to be the number 3·14.

In the example above $C = 3·14 \times 20 = 62·8$ cm.

If we want to use the radius instead of the diameter in the formula, then
$C = 2\pi r$
$\quad = 2 \times 3·14 \times 10$
$\quad = 62·8$ cm

π is often taken to be the number $\frac{22}{7}$ which can be useful in calculations where the radius is a multiple of 7, e.g. the circumference of a circle with radius 21 cm is $C = 2 \times \frac{22}{7} \times 21 = 132$ cm.

AREA

Area is a measure of how much surface is covered by a shape.

Area is measured by counting the number of squares a shape covers.

A square of side 1 cm covers 1 square cm (1 cm²) of surface.

Area of a Square

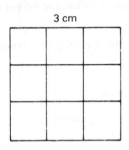

3 cm

The square in the diagram covers 9 cm², i.e. 3 rows of 3 squares.

The formula for the area of a square is $A = l^2$.

l^2 means $l \times l$ where l stands for the length of the side of the square.

Area of a Rectangle

6 cm

4 cm

The rectangle in the diagram covers 24 squares, i.e. 4 rows of 6 squares.

Since the edges of the rectangle are measured in cm the area is 24 cm².

A formula for the area of a rectangle is $A = lb$.

lb means $l \times b$ where l is the length of the rectangle and b is the breadth.

Area of a Right-angled Triangle

To find the area of a right-angled triangle we draw a rectangle round it as shown in the diagram here.

The area of the triangle can be seen to be half the area of its rectangle.

The area of the rectangle is $4 \times 3 = 12$ cm², so the area of the triangle is $\frac{1}{2} \times 12 = 6$ cm².

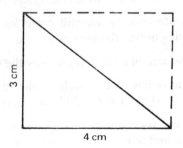

3 cm

4 cm

97

The area of any triangle can be found by the method on page 27 for the area of a triangle is always half the area of its rectangle.

The area of this triangle is $\frac{1}{2} \times 4 \times 5 = 10 \text{ cm}^2$.

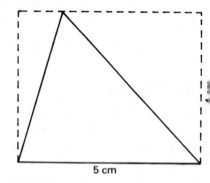

5 cm

The 5 cm line is called the *base* of the triangle.

The 4 cm line is called the *height* of the triangle.

A formula for the area of a triangle is $A = \frac{1}{2}bh$.

Area of a Circle

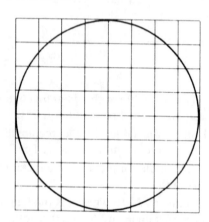

The diameter of the circle in the diagram is 8 cm.

The area of the circle is less than the area of the surrounding square.

The area of the circle is less than 64 cm².

Notice that we are still using squares to find the area even though we are trying to find the area of a circle.

The area of a circle is given by the formula $A = \pi r^2$.

The radius of the circle in the diagram is 4 cm so the area of the circle is $A = 3 \cdot 14 \times 4 \times 4 = 50 \cdot 2 \text{ cm}^2$ correct to three significant figures.

If you try counting the squares and bits of squares covered by the circle, you will find how difficult it would be to find the area without a formula.

VOLUME

Volume is a measure of how much space is occupied by a solid.

Volume can be measured by counting the number of cubes that would fill the space taken up by a solid.

Volume of a Cube

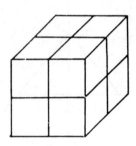

A cube whose edge is 1 cm long occupies 1 cm³ (1 cubic centimetre) of space.

The volume of any other solid whose edges are measured in cm is measured in cm³.

The volume of the cube in the diagram is 8 cm³.

The formula for finding the volume of a cube is $V = l^3$ where l^3 means $l \times l \times l$.

In this cube $V = 2^3 = 2 \times 2 \times 2 = 8$ cm³.

Volume of a Cuboid

The dimensions of the cuboid in the diagram are $3 \times 4 \times 5$ and the edges are measured in cm. The bottom of the cuboid has been filled with 1 cm cubes.

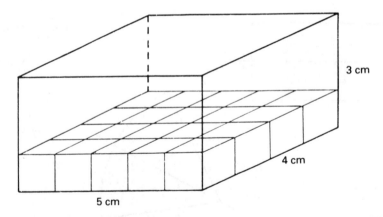

The bottom layer has $5 \times 4 = 20$ cubes. We need two more layers to fill the cuboid so 60 cubes are needed altogether.

The volume of the cuboid is 60 cm³.

The formula for the volume of a cuboid is $V = lbh$, i.e. length $\times$ breadth $\times$ height.

The volume of the above cuboid is $V = 5 \times 4 \times 3 = 60$ cm³.

LINE SYMMETRY

In the shapes below one side of the broken line looks like the mirror image of the other side. Shapes like these are said to have line symmetry.

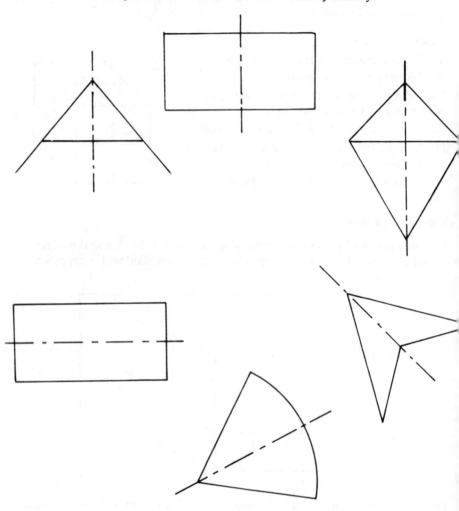

Some shapes have more than one line of symmetry as in the rectangles above.

When a shape is folded along its line of symmetry one side fits exactly on top of the other.

The line of symmetry is also called the *axis of symmetry*.

The square is an example of a figure with four axes of symmetry as shown in the diagram below.

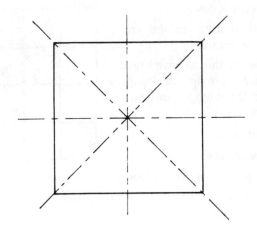

On the other hand it should be noted that the parallelogram has **NO** axis of symmetry.

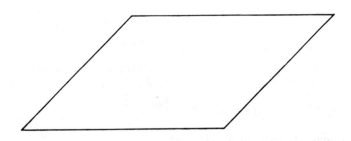

½-TURN AND ¼-TURN SYMMETRY

Look at the grid for a crossword puzzle in the diagram shown.

Turn the page upside down.

Notice that the pattern on the grid looks the same as before.

Figures like this are said to have ½-turn symmetry since turning the page upside down is the same as turning it through a ½ turn or 180°.

Look at the grid again.

Turn the page sideways.

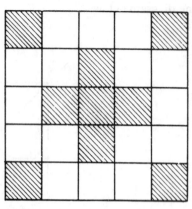

Notice that the pattern on the grid looks the same as before.

Figures like this are said to have ¼-turn symmetry since turning the page sideways is the same as turning it through a ¼ turn or 90°.

RATIO

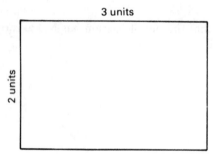

3 units

2 units

A ratio can be written in the form of a fraction.

The ratio of 2 to 3 can be written as $\frac{2}{3}$.

The ratio of 2 to 3 can also be written as 2 : 3.

The ratio of the breadth to the length of the rectangle in the diagram is $\frac{2}{3}$ or 2 : 3.

The ratio of the length to the breadth of the rectangle in the diagram is $\frac{3}{2}$ or 3 : 2.

In the triangle the ratio of the shortest side to the hypotenuse is $\frac{3}{5}$ or 3 : 5.

Notice that the fraction $\frac{6}{10}$ of the ratio has been reduced to its lowest terms $\frac{3}{5}$.

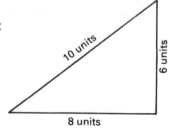

10 units

6 units

8 units

102

CONGRUENT FIGURES

Figures which are the same size and shape are said to be congruent to each other.

The two figures below are congruent to each other.

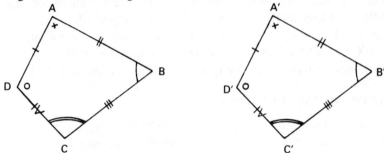

AB and A′B′ are called corresponding sides.

AD̂C and A′D̂′C′ are called corresponding angles.

All pairs of corresponding sides are equal, e.g. BC = B′C′.

All pairs of corresponding angles are equal, e.g. BĈD = B′Ĉ′D′.

Congruent figures will fit exactly on top of each other.

SIMILAR FIGURES

Figures which are the same shape but different size are said to be similar to each other.

The two figures below are similar to each other.

AB and A′B′ are called corresponding sides.

AD̂C and A′D̂′C′are called corresponding angles.

All pairs of corresponding angles are equal, e.g. BĈD = B′Ĉ′D′.

The ratios of pairs of corresponding sides are equal,

e.g. $\dfrac{AB}{A'B'} = \dfrac{BC}{B'C'} = \dfrac{CD}{C'D'} = \dfrac{DA}{D'A'}$

In the diagram above each ratio is equal to $\frac{1}{2}$.

ENLARGEMENT AND REDUCTION

In the diagram on page 103 A'B'C'D' is an enlargement of ABCD.

ABCD is a reduction of A'B'C'D'.

Since the sides of A'B'C'D' are twice as long as the corresponding sides in ABCD we have used a *scale factor* of 2, e.g. A'B' = 2AB.

Since the sides of ABCD are half as long as the corresponding sides of A'B'C'D' we have used a scale factor of $\frac{1}{2}$, e.g. AB = $\frac{1}{2}$A'B'.

A method of drawing the enlargement of a figure is shown below.

DRAWING ENLARGEMENTS

Draw the figure you want to enlarge (ABCD for example).

Mark a point as the *centre of enlargement* (O for example).

Choose a scale factor for the enlargement (2 for example).

Find the distance from the centre to a vertex of your figure (A for example).

Mark a point on the line through OA which is twice as long as OA.

Repeat the above for each vertex.

Join the new points to each other.

Follow the above steps with the diagram below.

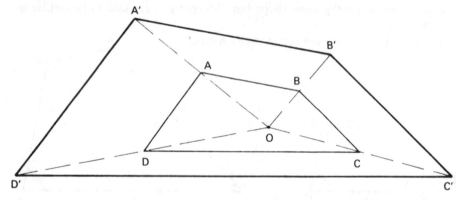

Notice that the centre, a vertex and its image all lie on a straight line.

Notice that in an enlargement (or a reduction) the corresponding sides are parallel.

Notice that in an enlargement (or a reduction) the figures are similar.

The same method can be used to make a reduction.

If we had started with A'B'C'D', centre O and scale factor $\frac{1}{2}$, we would mark points which were halfway between the centre and the vertex.

The diagram below shows an enlargement with centre O and scale factor 3. Notice that the centre does not have to be inside the figure you want to enlarge or reduce.

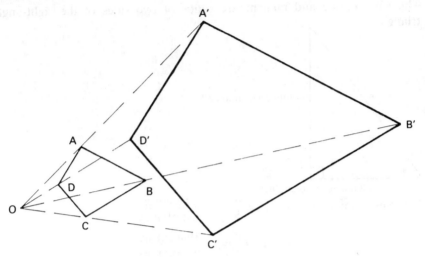

The diagram below shows a reduction of triangle AOB with centre O and scale factor $-\frac{1}{2}$.

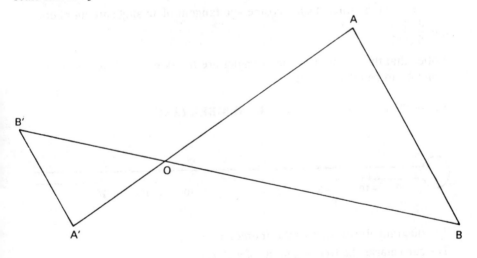

Notice that when the scale factor is negative the reduction (or enlargement) is on the opposite side of the centre from the original figure.

SINE, COSINE AND TANGENT

The sine, cosine and tangent of an angle can be read from a right-angled triangle.

The sine, cosine and tangent are ratios of two sides of the right-angled triangle.

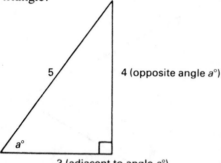

In the diagram above $\sin a° = \dfrac{4}{5} = \dfrac{\text{opposite side}}{\text{hypotenuse}}$

$\cos a° = \dfrac{3}{5} = \dfrac{\text{adjacent side}}{\text{hypotenuse}}$

$\tan a° = \dfrac{4}{3} = \dfrac{\text{opposite side}}{\text{adjacent side}}$

Notice that the ratios of sine, cosine and tangent of an angle are numbers, e.g. $\dfrac{4}{5}, \dfrac{3}{5}, \dfrac{4}{3}$.

Notice that the sine and cosine of angles are fractions, i.e. less than 1, but the tangent can be greater than 1.

NEGATIVE NUMBERS AND THE NUMBER LINE

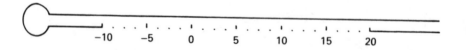

The diagram above shows a thermometer.

The zero marks the freezing point of water.

When the temperature rises above freezing point the readings on the thermometer will be on the right of the zero mark.

106

The numbers to the right of zero are positive numbers.

When the temperature falls below freezing the readings on the thermometer will be on the left of the zero mark.

The numbers to the left of zero are negative numbers.

When the temperature falls 5°C below freezing the thermometer will read –5.

The scale on the thermometer is a number line.

To show numbers greater than –3 on a number line we draw the diagram below.

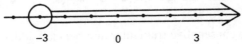

To show numbers less than or equal to –3 we draw the diagram below.

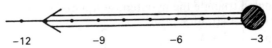

Notice that when we show a number greater than (or less than) we use an open circle.

When we show a number greater than (or less than) or equal to we shade the circle.

SQUARE NUMBERS

When a number is multiplied by itself we say we have squared the number.

The square of 5 is $5 \times 5 = 25$.

5×5 or 25 can be written as 5^2 (5 squared).

When we want to talk about the square of a number without saying which number we mean we can call the number x and its square is called x^2.

Any letter can be used to stand for any number, e.g. n and n^2.

Square numbers can be shown as a pattern of dots.

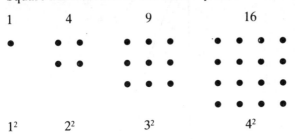

107

TRIANGULAR NUMBERS

The set of numbers 1, 3, 6, 10, ... are called triangular numbers and can be shown in a pattern of dots.

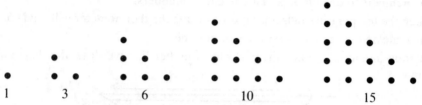

Notice that if two consecutive triangular numbers are added together we get a square number, e.g. $1 + 3 = 4$, $3 + 6 = 9$, $6 + 10 = 16$, $10 + 15 = 25$, etc.

PYTHAGORAS' THEOREM

In any right-angled triangle the hypotenuse squared is equal to the sum of the squares of the other two sides.

In this diagram $5^2 = 3^2 + 4^2$.

Since this is true for any right-angled triangle we can use letters to stand for the lengths of the sides of the right-angled triangle.

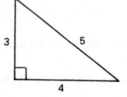

In this triangle $a^2 = b^2 + c^2$.

If we know the sizes of two of the sides of a right-angled triangle we can calculate the third side.

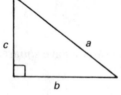

In this diagram
$$a^2 = 12^2 + 5^2$$
$$= 144 + 25$$
$$= 169$$
$$= 13^2$$
$$a = 13$$

In this diagram
$$13^2 = 12^2 + x^2$$
$$x^2 = 13^2 - 12^2$$
$$= 169 - 144$$
$$= 25$$
$$= 5^2$$
$$x = 5$$

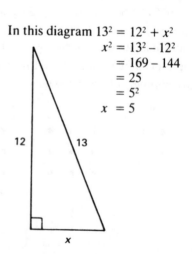

RELATED ANGLES

When parallel lines are cut by a straight line the angles formed are related to each other.

CORRESPONDING ANGLES

The angles marked $a°$ are equal to each other and are called corresponding angles.

All the pairs of angles with the same names are equal and corresponding.

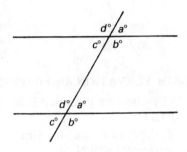

ALTERNATE ANGLES

The pairs of angles with the same names are equal to each other and are called alternate angles.

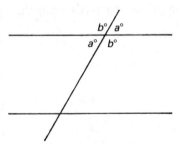

VERTICALLY OPPOSITE ANGLES

The pairs of angles marked with the same names are equal to each other and are called vertically opposite angles.

ALLIED ANGLES

Allied angles are supplementary, i.e. add up to 180°.

In the diagram $d° + e° = 180°$.

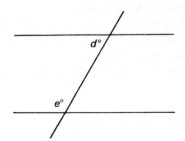

109

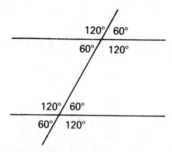

Notice that if you are given the size of one of the angles in the diagram on page 109 then you can find the size of every other angle in the diagram, e.g. if $d = 60$ then $e = 180 - 60 = 120$, then by using the previous types of angles all the others can be found as shown in the diagram.

ANGLES OF ELEVATION AND DEPRESSION

Angles of elevation are measured from the horizontal UP.

Angles of depression are measured from the horizontal DOWN.

This diagram shows a point P at an angle of elevation $x°$ from A and a point A at an angle of depression $x°$ from P.

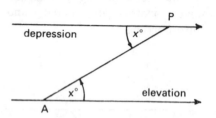

COORDINATES

The position of a point on a plane is given by a pair of coordinates (x, y) where x and y stand for numbers.

Coordinates give the position of a point on a *cartesian diagram*.

A cartesian diagram has an x-axis which is perpendicular to a y-axis.

The point where the x-axis meets the y-axis is called the *origin* and is given the letter O.

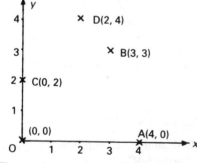

All the positions on the cartesian diagram are found by measuring from the *origin*, O.

The first number in the brackets is the x coordinate and the second number the y coordinate.

The point (x, y) is found by measuring along the x-axis and then measuring parallel to the y-axis.

The diagram shows the points O(0, 0), A(4, 0), B(3, 3), C(0, 2), D(2, 4).

The x-axis goes across the page. The y-axis goes up the page.

Arrows at the end of the x- and y-axes point in the direction of greater numbers.

A capital letter is used to name a point.

Coordinates are always in brackets.

There is always a comma between the x and the y coordinates.

EQUATION OF A STRAIGHT LINE 1

The diagram below shows a straight line and some points on the line are named.

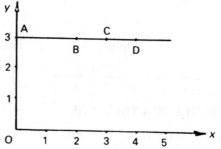

A has coordinates (0, 3).
B has coordinates (2, 3).
C has coordinates (3, 3).
D has coordinates (4, 3).

Since every point on this line has a y-coordinate of 3 we say that the line has equation $y = 3$.

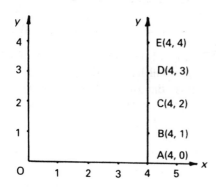

In the same way this diagram has equation $x = 4$ since all the x-coordinates are equal to 4.

This diagram shows the points O(0, 0), A(1, 1), B(2, 2), C(3, 3), D(4, 4).

Since the y-coordinate is always equal to the x-coordinate the line is said to have equation $y = x$.

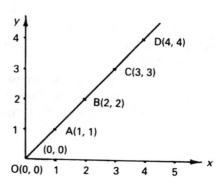

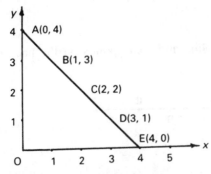

This diagram shows the points A(0, 4), B(1, 3), C(2, 2), D(3, 1), E(4, 0).

Here the x-coordinate added to the y-coordinate always gives the answer 4.

The equation of the line is $x + y = 4$.

ALTITUDES OF A TRIANGLE

A straight line from a vertex of a triangle perpendicular to the opposite side is called an altitude of the triangle. Every triangle has three altitudes.

In this diagram AX, BY and CZ are the three altitudes of triangle ABC.

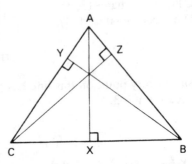

Notice that the three altitudes intersect (cut each other) at the same point.

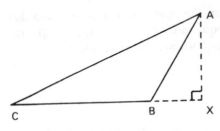

In an obtuse-angled triangle an altitude will lie outside the triangle as in this diagram where AX is an altitude of triangle ABC.

MEDIANS OF A TRIANGLE

A median of a triangle is a straight line from a vertex to the mid-point of the opposite side. Every triangle has three medians.

The diagram shows triangle ABC and a median AM.

A median divides the triangle into two equal areas. In this diagram the area of triangle ABM = the area of triangle ACM.

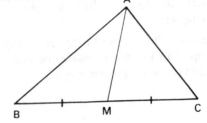

This diagram shows triangle ABC and the three medians AX, BY, CZ.

Notice that the three medians intersect at the same point, G.

The point G is called the centroid of the triangle.

The centroid divides each median in the ratio 2 : 1, i.e. AG = 2GX, BG = 2GY, CG = 2GZ.

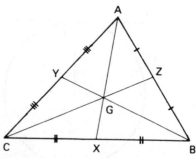

If ABC were a setsquare then you could balance it on the point G.

THE CIRCLE 2

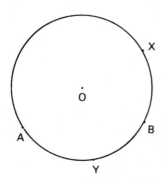

AYB is the *minor arc* of the circle with centre O.

AXB is the *major arc* of the circle with centre O.

AB is a *chord* of the circle with centre O.

The diameter of a circle is the longest chord.

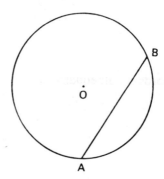

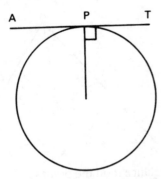

APT is a *tangent* to the circle at P.

A tangent touches the circle at only one point.

A tangent is perpendicular to a radius of the circle at the point of contact, P.

A line from the centre of a circle to the mid-point of a chord is perpendicular to the chord.

A line from the centre of a circle perpendicular to a chord bisects the chord.

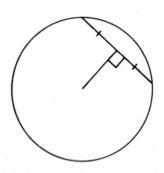

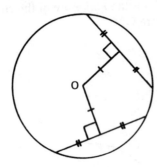

Equal chords are equidistant (the same distance) from the centre of a circle.

Chords equidistant from the centre of a circle are equal.

Equal chords cut off equal arcs.

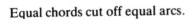

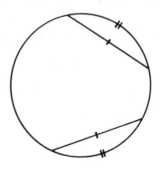

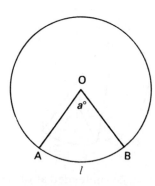

AOB is a *sector* of the circle with centre O.

Arc AB *subtends* $A\hat{O}B$ at the centre O.

The length, l, of the minor arc AB is given by the formula $l = \dfrac{a}{360} \times 2\pi r$.

The area of the sector AOB is given by the formula

$$\text{Area} = \dfrac{a}{360} \times \pi r^2.$$

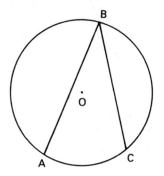

The minor arc AC subtends the angle ABC at the circumference of the circle with centre O.

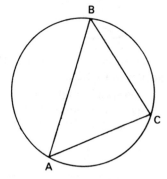

The chord AC subtends the angle ABC at the circumference of the circle.

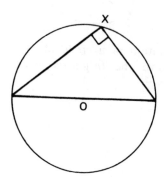

The diameter of a circle subtends a right angle at the circumference.

The angle in a semi-circle is a right angle.

Angles subtended at the circumference of a circle by the same arc are equal.

Angles subtended at the circumference by the same chord are equal.

Angles subtended at the circumference by equal arcs or chords are equal.

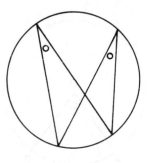

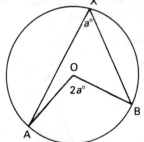

The angle subtended at the centre of a circle is twice the angle subtended at the circumference by the same arc or chord.

$\hat{AOB} = 2A\hat{X}B$ in the diagram.

ABCD is a *cyclic quadrilateral*.

The opposite angles of a cyclic quadrilateral are supplementary.

$\hat{DAB} + \hat{DCB} = 180°$
$\hat{ABC} + \hat{ADC} = 180°$.

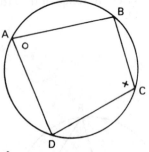

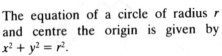

$\hat{BCX}$ is an *exterior angle* of the cyclic quadrilateral ABCD.

The exterior angle of a cyclic quadrilateral is equal to the interior opposite angle. $\hat{BCX} = \hat{DAB}$.

The equation of a circle of radius r and centre the origin is given by $x^2 + y^2 = r^2$.

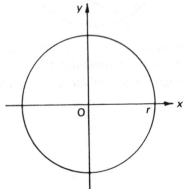

SINE, COSINE AND TANGENT OF 30°, 45° AND 60°

The sine, cosine and tangent of 45° can be read from the right-angled triangle below.

$$\sin 45° = \frac{1}{\sqrt{2}}$$

$$\cos 45° = \frac{1}{\sqrt{2}}$$

$$\tan 45° = 1$$

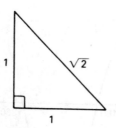

The sine, cosine and tangent of 30° and 60° can be read from the right-angled triangle below.

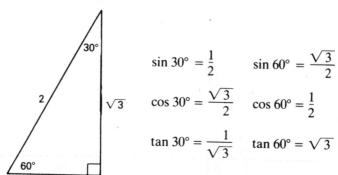

$$\sin 30° = \frac{1}{2} \qquad \sin 60° = \frac{\sqrt{3}}{2}$$

$$\cos 30° = \frac{\sqrt{3}}{2} \qquad \cos 60° = \frac{1}{2}$$

$$\tan 30° = \frac{1}{\sqrt{3}} \qquad \tan 60° = \sqrt{3}$$

Note that $\dfrac{\sin a°}{\cos a°} = \tan a°$

and $\sin^2 a° + \cos^2 a° = 1$

GRAPHS OF SIN x°, COS x° AND TAN x°

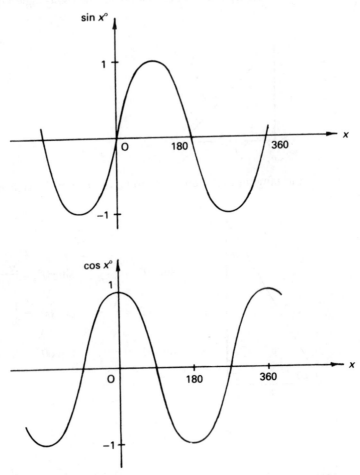

The graph of sin x° and cos x° repeat the same pattern every 360°.

The *period* of the sine and cosine is 360°.

The maximum value of the sine is 1.

The maximum value of the cosine is 1.

The minimum value of the sine is −1.

The minimum value of the cosine is −1.

The graph of the sine is the same shape as the graph of the cosine when translated 90° to the left.

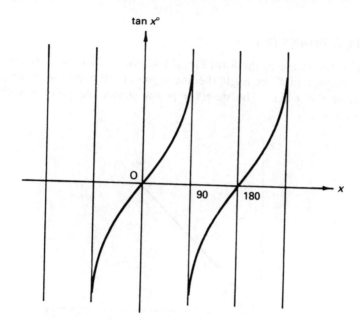

The graph of the tangent repeats its pattern every 180°.
The period of the tangent is 180°.
The tangent has no maximum or minimum value.

The following diagram will help to remind you which trigonometric ratios are positive or negative for angles in each quadrant.

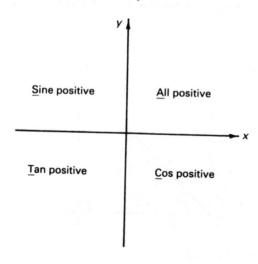

POLAR COORDINATES

Polar coordinates are of the form $P(r, a°)$ where r tells how far the point P is from the origin and $a°$ the angle the line segment OP makes with the positive direction of the x-axis. The diagram below shows the point P with polar coordinates $(r, a°)$.

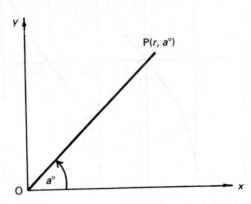

Notice that r is **not** the same as the x-coordinate nor is a the same as the y-coordinate.

r and $a°$ can be used to find the x- and y-coordinates in the form $(r \cos a°, r \sin a°)$. Here $x = r \cos a°$ and $y = r \sin a°$. If you read off the ratios of $\sin a°$ and $\cos a°$ from the diagram below you will see why this is the case.

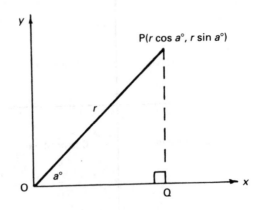

$PQ = r \sin a°$ and $OQ = r \cos a°$.

120

DISTANCE FORMULA

The distance between two points $A(x_A, y_A)$ and $B(x_B, y_B)$ is found by the formula $d = \sqrt{(y_B - y_A)^2 + (x_B - x_A)^2}$

Example: Find the distance between $A(3, 1)$ and $B(6, 5)$.

The diagram shows that the formula comes from the theorem of Pythagoras.

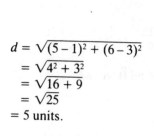

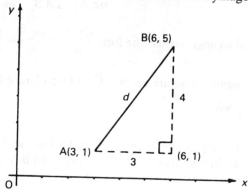

$$d = \sqrt{(5 - 1)^2 + (6 - 3)^2}$$
$$= \sqrt{4^2 + 3^2}$$
$$= \sqrt{16 + 9}$$
$$= \sqrt{25}$$
$$= 5 \text{ units.}$$

MID-POINT OF A LINE SEGMENT

If A is (x_A, y_A) and B is (x_B, y_B) then the mid-point of AB has coordinates $\left(\dfrac{x_A + x_B}{2}, \dfrac{y_A + y_B}{2}\right)$.

For example, the mid-point of the line joining $A(3, 5)$ and $B(7, 1)$ is $\left(\dfrac{3 + 7}{2}, \dfrac{5 + 1}{2}\right) = (5, 3)$.

THE AREA OF A TRIANGLE (TRIG.)

Notice that in the diagram the sides are named with the same letters as the angles opposite them but with small letters.

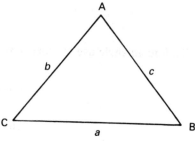

The area of the triangle ABC $= \frac{1}{2}ab \sin \hat{C}$
$$= \frac{1}{2}bc \sin \hat{A}$$
$$= \frac{1}{2}ac \sin \hat{B}$$

Notice that all three letters of the triangle's name occur in each version of the formula.

THE SINE RULE

The sine rule is used when we are given a side and an angle of the same name and one other side or angle of a triangle.

To find a side we use the form $\dfrac{a}{\sin \hat{A}} = \dfrac{b}{\sin \hat{B}} = \dfrac{c}{\sin \hat{C}}$

To find an angle we use the form $\dfrac{\sin \hat{A}}{a} = \dfrac{\sin \hat{B}}{b} = \dfrac{\sin \hat{C}}{c}$

For example, if we are given c, $\hat{C}$ and b and have to find $\hat{B}$ we use

$\dfrac{\sin \hat{B}}{b} = \dfrac{\sin \hat{C}}{c}$.

Always write the thing you have to find as the first term in the formula. For example, in the formula above we wrote $\sin \hat{B}$ first since we wanted to find $\hat{B}$.

THE COSINE RULE

The cosine rule is used when we are given three sides or two sides and the included angle (i.e. the angle between the two given sides).

To find sides we use the form $a^2 = b^2 + c^2 - 2bc \cos \hat{A}$
$$b^2 = a^2 + c^2 - 2ac \cos \hat{B}$$
$$c^2 = a^2 + b^2 - 2ab \cos \hat{C}$$

If the angle is obtuse then use the fact that $\cos x° = -\cos (180 - x)°$,

e.g. $a^2 = b^2 + c^2 - 2bc \cos 150°$ becomes
$$a^2 = b^2 + c^2 + 2bc \cos 30°.$$

To find an angle use the form $\cos \hat{A} = \dfrac{b^2 + c^2 - a^2}{2bc}$
$$\cos \hat{B} = \dfrac{a^2 + c^2 - b^2}{2ac}$$
$$\cos \hat{C} = \dfrac{a^2 + b^2 - c^2}{2ab}$$

If the right-hand side of the above formula is negative then the angle is obtuse.

VARIATION

Words	Symbols	Form of equation
x varies as y	$x \propto y$	$x = ky$
x varies directly as y	$x \propto y$	$x = ky$
x varies inversely as y	$x \propto \dfrac{1}{y}$	$x = \dfrac{k}{y}$
x varies directly as y and z	$x \propto yz$	$x = kyz$
x varies directly as y and inversely as z	$x \propto \dfrac{y}{z}$	$x = \dfrac{ky}{z}$
x varies directly as the root of y and inversely as the square of z	$x \propto \dfrac{\sqrt{y}}{z^2}$	$x = \dfrac{k\sqrt{y}}{z^2}$

The first step is to substitute for x and y (and z) in order to find k then use this value of k for the rest of the problem.

INDICES

$x^a x^b = x^{a+b}$　　　　e.g. $x^3 x^2 = x^{3+2} = x^5$

$\dfrac{x^a}{x^b} = x^{a-b}$　　　　e.g. $\dfrac{x^3}{x^2} = x^{3-2} = x^1 = x$

$(x^a)^b = x^{ab}$　　　　e.g. $(x^3)^2 = x^6$

$x^0 = 1$　　　　e.g. $3^0 = 1$, $(2y+3)^0 = 1$

$x^{\frac{1}{2}} = \sqrt{x}$　　　　e.g. $9^{\frac{1}{2}} = \sqrt{9} = 3$

$x^{\frac{2}{3}} = (\sqrt[3]{x})^2$　　　　e.g. $8^{\frac{2}{3}} = 2^2 = 4$

$x^{-3} = \dfrac{1}{x^3}$　　　　e.g. $2^{-3} = \dfrac{1}{2^3} = \dfrac{1}{8}$

$x^{-\frac{1}{3}} = \dfrac{1}{x^{\frac{1}{3}}} = \dfrac{1}{\sqrt[3]{x}}$　　　　e.g. $27^{-\frac{1}{3}} = \dfrac{1}{27^{\frac{1}{3}}} = \dfrac{1}{3}$

$x^{-\frac{2}{3}} = \dfrac{1}{x^{\frac{2}{3}}}$　　　　e.g. $27^{-\frac{2}{3}} = \dfrac{1}{27^{\frac{2}{3}}} = \dfrac{1}{3^2} = \dfrac{1}{9}$

CHANGING THE SUBJECT OF A FORMULA

1. Get all terms with the subject to the numerator.
2. Get all terms with the subject out of brackets.
3. Get all terms with the subject to one side of the formula.
4. Take the subject out as the common factor.
5. Divide both sides of the formula by the coefficient of the subject.

Example: Change the subject of the formula $ax = \dfrac{p + r}{q + r}$ to r.

1. $ax(q + r) = p + r$
2. $axq + axr = p + r$
3. $axr - r = p - axq$
4. $(ax - 1)r = p - axq$
5. $r = \dfrac{p - axq}{ax - 1}$

EQUATION OF A STRAIGHT LINE 2

The general equation of a straight line is of the form $y = mx + c$.
m is the *gradient* or slope of the line and c is where the line cuts the y-axis.

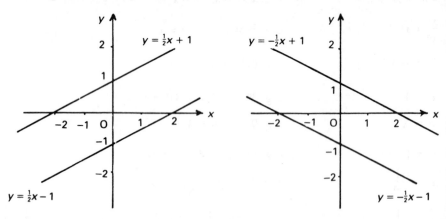

Notice that when the gradients are equal the lines are parallel.

Notice that when the line makes an acute angle with the positive direction of the x-axis the gradient is positive.

Notice that when the line makes an obtuse angle with the positive direction of the x-axis the gradient is negative.

From graphs such as those on page 124 the gradient can be read off as

$$m = \frac{\text{number of units cut off } y\text{-axis}}{\text{number of units cut off } x\text{-axis}},$$ the sign of m depending on the angle made with the positive direction of the x-axis.

The gradient of a line which goes through the points A(x_A, y_A), B(x_B, y_B) is
$$m = \frac{y_B - y_A}{x_B - x_A}.$$

The equation of a straight line may be in the form $ax + by = c$, e.g. $3x + 2y = 6$.

To draw the graph of a line we need to know the coordinates of only two points on the line, $(x, 0)$ and $(0, y)$.

Substituting 0 for y in the equation we get $3x + 2(0) = 6$ giving $3x = 6$ and $x = 2$, so $(2, 0)$ lies on the line.

Substituting 0 for x in the equation we get $3(0) + 2y = 6$ giving $2y = 6$ and $y = 3$, so $(0, 3)$ lies on the line. The graph is shown.

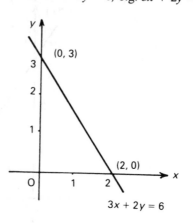

$$3x + 2y = 6$$

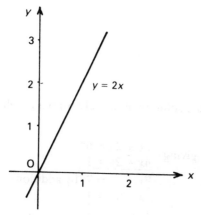

When there is no constant in the equation then the line goes through the origin so we can use $(0, 0)$ as one point on the line then substitute any value for x, e.g. $x = 1$ for the second point.

The graph of $y = 2x$ is shown.

SYSTEMS OF EQUATIONS

The solution to a system of equations can be shown on a graph, e.g.

solve $3x + 2y = 6$

$\quad 2x - y = \frac{1}{2}$

The solution is given by the coordinates of the point of intersection of the two lines on the graph which is shown.

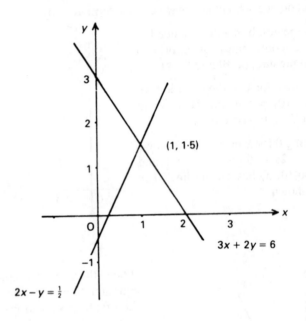

Since it might be difficult to read off the solution accurately from a graph we can use algebra as follows:

$3x + 2y = 6$

$2x - y = \frac{1}{2}$ (multiply by 2)

giving

$3x + 2y = 6$

$\underline{4x - 2y = 1}$

$7x \quad\quad = 7$ (by addition)

$x \quad\quad = 1$

By now substituting $x = 1$ in either of the equations we can find y, e.g.

$3(1) + 2y = 6$ giving $2y = 3$, so $y = \dfrac{3}{2} = 1.5$ as before.

INEQUATIONS (LINEAR)

1. Get rid of denominators by multiplying throughout by the L.C.M.
2. Get all terms out of brackets.
3. Get all x terms together on left-hand side of equation.
4. Get all constants to right-hand side of equation.
5. Divide both sides by the coefficient of x.

Example: Solve $\frac{5}{6}(x + 2) - \frac{2}{3}(2x - 3) < \frac{1}{2}$

1. $5(x + 2) - 4(2x - 3) < 3$ (L.C.M. of 6, 3 and 2 is 6)
2. $5x + 10 - 8x + 12 < 3$
3. x terms are on the left-hand side already
4. $-3x < -19$

*5. $x > \dfrac{19}{3}$

* Notice that when an inequation is multiplied or divided by a negative number then the sign of the inequation changes, i.e. $<$ becomes $>$ and vice versa.

EXPANDING BRACKETS

1. $3(x + 2)$ $= 3x + 6$
2. $-3(x + 2)$ $= -3x - 6$
3. $x(x + 2)$ $= x^2 + 2x$
4. $-x(x + 2)$ $= -x^2 - 2x$
5. $x(2 - x)$ $= 2x - x^2$
6. $-x(2 - x)$ $= -2x + x^2$
7. $-3x(2x - 4)$ $= -6x^2 + 12x$
8. $(x + 2)(x - 3)$ $= x^2 + 2x - 3x - 6$
   $= x^2 - x - 6$
9. $(2x - 1)(3x + 1) = 6x^2 + 2x - 3x - 1$
   $= 6x^2 - x - 1$
10. $(x + 2)^2$ $= x^2 + 4x + 4$
11. $(x - 3)^2$ $= x^2 - 6x + 9$
12. $(3x - 2)^2$ $= 9x^2 - 12x + 4$
13. $(2x - 3y)^2$ $= 4x^2 - 12xy + 9y^2$

FACTORISING

1.   **Common Factor**

     (i) $3x + 6y = 3(x + 2y)$

     (ii) $3x^2 + 6xy = 3x(x + 2y)$

     (iii) $3x^3 + 6x^2 + 3x = 3x(x^2 + 2x + 1)$

2.   **Difference of Two Squares**

     (i) $x^2 - y^2 = (x - y)(x + y)$

     (ii) $4x^2 - 9y^2 = (2x - 3y)(2x + 3y)$

     (iii) $16x^4 - 81y^4 = (4x^2 - 9y^2)(4x^2 + 9y^2)$
                             $= (2x - 3y)(2x + 3y)(4x^2 + 9y^2)$

Always take out the common factor first, e.g.

$12x^2 - 27y^2 = 3(4x^2 - 9y^2)$

$= 3(2x - 3y)(2x + 3y)$

3. **Quadratic form**

    (i) $x^2 + 2x + 1 = (x + 1)(x + 1)$
$$= (x + 1)^2$$
   (ii) $x^2 + 5x + 6 = (x + 3)(x + 2)$
  (iii) $x^2 - 5x + 6 = (x - 3)(x - 2)$
  (iv) $x^2 - x - 6 = (x - 3)(x + 2)$
   (v) $x^2 + x - 6 = (x + 3)(x - 2)$
  (vi) $x^2 + (p + q)x + pq = (x + p)(x + q)$

Notice that the coefficient of x in the quadratic form is the sum of the two constants in the brackets and that the constant in the quadratic form is the product of the two constants in the brackets.

When the constant in the quadratic form is positive both signs in the brackets are the same as that of the coefficient of x in the quadratic form.

When the constant in the quadratic form is negative the signs in the brackets are different from each other.

QUADRATIC EQUATIONS

$2x^2 + 3x + 1 = 0$ is a quadratic equation. It can be solved by factorising the left-hand side of the equation giving

$(2x + 1)(x + 1) = 0$
so either $2x + 1 = 0$ or $x + 1 = 0$
giving $x = -\frac{1}{2}$ or $x = -1$

If the left-hand side of a quadratic equation cannot be factorised then a formula is used.

A quadratic equation has the shape $ax^2 + bx + c = 0$.

The formula is $x = \dfrac{-b \pm \sqrt{b^2 - 4(a)(c)}}{2a}$

For the example above $x = \dfrac{-3 \pm \sqrt{9 - 4(2)(1)}}{2(2)}$

$$= \dfrac{-3 \pm \sqrt{9 - 8}}{4}$$

$$= \dfrac{-3 \pm 1}{4}$$

$$= \dfrac{-3 + 1}{4} \text{ or } \dfrac{-3 - 1}{4}$$

$$= \dfrac{-2}{4} \text{ or } \dfrac{-4}{4}$$

$$= -\tfrac{1}{2} \text{ or } -1 \text{ as before by factorisation.}$$

THE PARABOLA (Graph of a Quadratic Function)

$f(x) = 2x^2 + 3x + 1$ is a quadratic function. Its graph is a parabola.

The sketch of the graph is shown below.

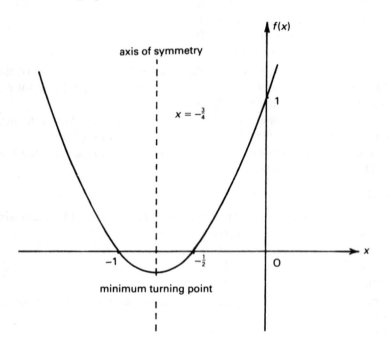

The points $(-1, 0)$ and $(-\frac{1}{2}, 0)$ where the graph cuts the x-axis are found by making $f(x) = 0$

i.e. $\quad 0 = 2x^2 + 3x + 1$

giving $\quad 0 = (2x + 1)(x + 1)$

so $\qquad 2x + 1 = 0 \quad$ or $\quad x + 1 = 0$

and $\qquad\quad x = -\frac{1}{2} \quad$ or $\quad x = -1$

The constant, 1, of $f(x)$ tells where the graph cuts the $f(x)$-axis, $(0, 1)$ in the diagram.

The parabola always has an axis of symmetry which goes through the maximum or minimum turning point.

If the coefficient of x^2 is positive the graph has a minimum turning point.

If the coefficient of x^2 is negative the graph has a maximum turning point.

130

A few more graphs of quadratic functions are shown below.

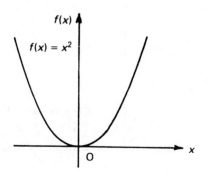

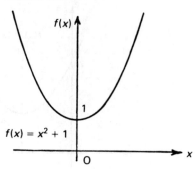

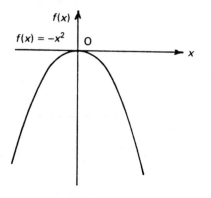

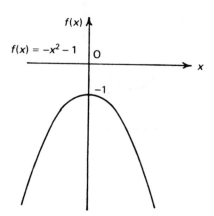

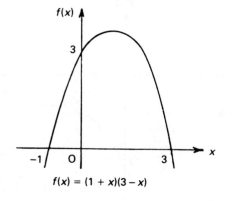

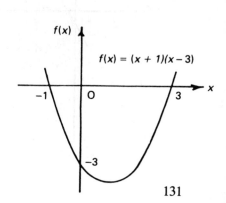

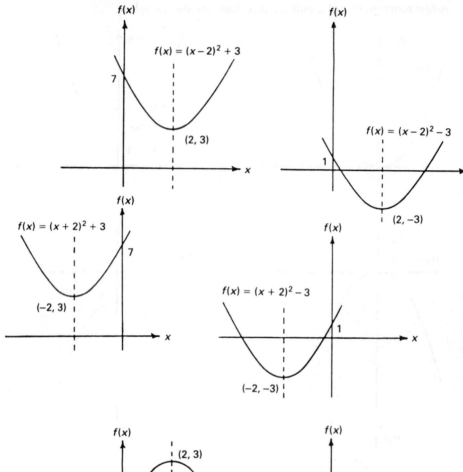

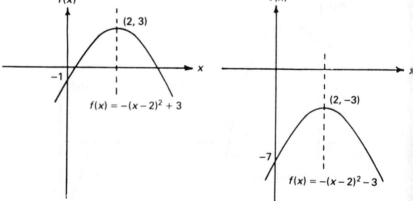

QUADRATIC INEQUATIONS

$x^2 + x - 6 < 0$ is a quadratic inequation.

To solve the inequation we first sketch its graph.

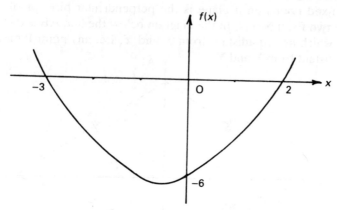

The part of the graph which lies below the x-axis is where the value of $f(x) < 0$. The value of x on any part of this section is $-3 < x < 2$.

The same graph is used to solve $x^2 + x - 6 \geqslant 0$.

This time the parts of the graph which lie on or above the x-axis are where the value of $f(x) \geqslant 0$. The value of x on these two sections is $x \leqslant -3$ and $x \geqslant 2$.

The solutions are shown on the number lines below.

$x^2 + x - 6 < 0$

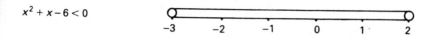

$x^2 + x - 6 \geqslant 0$

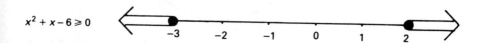

LOCUS

The locus of a point is all the possible positions of the point when it moves according to a given rule.

For example, the locus of a point which is equidistant (the same distance) from two fixed points on a plane is the perpendicular bisector of the line joining the two fixed points. In the diagram below the line AB is the locus of the points which are equidistant from X and Y, i.e. any point P on the line AB is equidistant from X and Y.

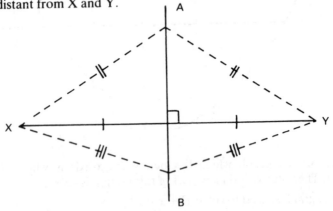

The locus of a point which is equidistant from a fixed point is a circle where the fixed point is the centre of the circle and the fixed distance is the radius of the circle. The diagram below shows the locus of a point which is three units from a fixed point O.

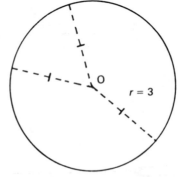

If the above locus were in three dimensions then the locus would be the surface of a sphere where the fixed point would be the centre of the sphere and the fixed distance the radius of the sphere.

SURDS

If x is a rational number but $\sqrt{x}$ is not then $\sqrt{x}$ is called a surd.

Laws of surds.

$\sqrt{a} + \sqrt{a} = 2\sqrt{a}$ e.g. $\sqrt{3} + \sqrt{3} = 2\sqrt{3}$

$3\sqrt{a} - \sqrt{a} = 2\sqrt{a}$ e.g. $3\sqrt{3} - \sqrt{3} = 2\sqrt{3}$

$\sqrt{a} \times \sqrt{a} = a$ e.g. $\sqrt{3} \times \sqrt{3} = 3$

$2\sqrt{a} \times 3\sqrt{a} = 6a$ e.g. $2\sqrt{3} \times 3\sqrt{3} = 6 \times 3 = 18$

$\sqrt{a} \times \sqrt{b} = \sqrt{ab}$ e.g. $\sqrt{3} \times \sqrt{5} = \sqrt{15}$

$2\sqrt{a} \times 3\sqrt{b} = 6\sqrt{ab}$ e.g. $2\sqrt{3} \times 3\sqrt{5} = 6\sqrt{15}$

$\dfrac{6\sqrt{a}}{2} = 3\sqrt{a}$ e.g. $\dfrac{6\sqrt{3}}{2} = 3\sqrt{3}$

$\dfrac{\sqrt{a}}{\sqrt{b}} = \sqrt{\dfrac{a}{b}}$ e.g. $\dfrac{\sqrt{3}}{\sqrt{5}} = \sqrt{\dfrac{3}{5}}$

$\dfrac{\sqrt{ab}}{\sqrt{b}} = \sqrt{a}$ e.g. $\dfrac{\sqrt{15}}{\sqrt{5}} = \dfrac{\sqrt{3.5}}{\sqrt{5}} = \sqrt{3}$

$$\dfrac{\sqrt{375}}{\sqrt{5}} = \sqrt{\dfrac{25 \times 3 \times 5}{5}} = 5\sqrt{3}$$

ALGEBRAIC FRACTIONS

1. $\dfrac{1}{x} + \dfrac{1}{y}$ compare $\dfrac{1}{3} + \dfrac{1}{5}$

  $\Leftrightarrow$ $\dfrac{y + x}{xy}$ $\dfrac{5 + 3}{3 \times 5}$

2. $\dfrac{3}{x^2} + \dfrac{2}{y}$ compare $\dfrac{3}{4} + \dfrac{2}{3}$

  $\Leftrightarrow$ $\dfrac{3y + 2x^2}{x^2 y}$ $\dfrac{3 \times 3 + 2 \times 4}{4 \times 3}$

3. $$\frac{3}{xy} + \frac{2}{y} \qquad \text{compare} \qquad \frac{3}{5 \times 7} + \frac{2}{7}$$

$$\Leftrightarrow \quad \frac{3 + 2x}{xy} \qquad\qquad\qquad \frac{3 + 2 \times 5}{5 \times 7}$$

For subtraction simply change '+' to '−'.

4. $$\frac{3}{x-1} - \frac{2}{x}$$

$$\Leftrightarrow \quad \frac{3x - 2(x-1)}{x(x-1)}$$

$$\Leftrightarrow \quad \frac{x+2}{x(x-1)}$$

5. $$\frac{x}{y} \times \frac{2}{z} = \frac{2x}{yz} \qquad \text{compare} \qquad \frac{3}{5} \times \frac{2}{7} = \frac{2 \times 3}{5 \times 7}$$

6. $$\frac{x}{y} \times \frac{3x}{z} = \frac{3x^2}{yz}$$

7. $$\frac{x^{\cancel{1}}}{y} \times \frac{z}{\cancel{x}_1} = \frac{z}{y} \qquad \text{compare} \qquad \frac{\cancel{3}^1}{5} \times \frac{7}{\cancel{3}_1} = \frac{7}{5}$$

8. $$\frac{x-3}{y} \times \frac{x}{z} = \frac{x(x-3)}{yz}$$

9. $$\frac{x^2-4}{y} \times \frac{z}{x+2} = \frac{(x-2)\cancel{(x+2)}^1}{y} \times \frac{z}{\cancel{(x+2)}_1} = \frac{z(x-2)}{y}$$

10. $$\frac{x^2-4}{y+3} \times \frac{y^2+4y+3}{x-2} = \frac{^1\cancel{(x-2)}(x+2)}{\cancel{(y+3)}_1} \times \frac{^1\cancel{(y+3)}(y+1)}{\cancel{(x-2)}_1}$$

$$= (x+2)(y+1)$$

To simplify algebraic fractions:

(a) Factorise numerator.

(b) Factorise denominator.

(c) Cancel common factors between numerator and denominator.

Graph of $y \geqslant 2x + 3$

To draw the graph of a linear inequation first draw the line, e.g. $y = 2x + 3$.

The solutions to the inequation will lie on and above the line.

The solutions to the inequation $y < 2x + 3$ will lie anywhere below the line.

The graph is shown below.

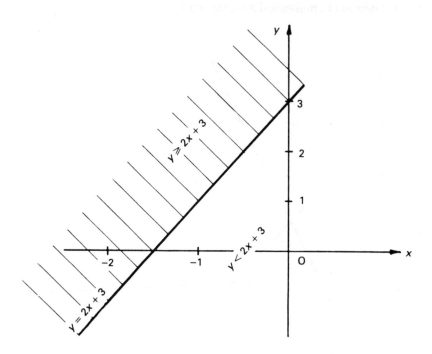

Linear Programming

A pupil can do an algebra question in five minutes and a geometry question in four minutes.

He must do at least twelve questions for homework.

He must do at least twice as many geometry questions as algebra questions.

How many algebra and geometry questions should he do to spend the least time doing homework?

Let x be the number of algebra questions.

Let y be the number of geometry questions.

$x > 0$, $y > 0$, x and y are whole numbers.

$x + y \geqslant 12$ (at least twelve questions).

$2x - y \leqslant 0$ (at least twice as many geometry as algebra questions).

$(5x + 4y)$ minutes to minimised for homework time.

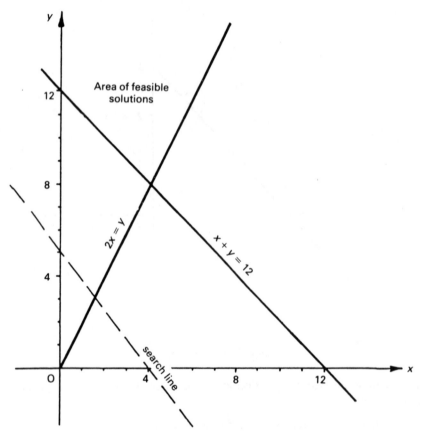

The point (1, 11) lies in the area where $x + y \geqslant 12$ and $2x - y \leqslant 0$.

The minimum time is $(5 \times 1) + (4 \times 11) = 49$ minutes for the pupil to do one algebra question and eleven geometry questions.

The point (1, 11) was found by drawing a 'search line' with equation $5x + 4y = K$ and then finding the first point reached in the area of feasible solutions by such a line, e.g. if the line $5x + 4y = 20$ is drawn it is then moved parallel to this line till the area is reached.

Note that it is assumed that the pupil must do both algebra and geometry questions so the point (0, 12) is ignored which is the first point reached by the 'search line'. The next point reached where x and y are whole numbers is the point (1, 11) which gives the solution.

Functional Notation

The y-axis is sometimes named the $f(x)$-axis as in the diagram below.

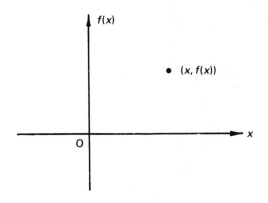

Any point on the diagram will have coordinates $(x, f(x))$, e.g. $(1, f(1))$, $(-2, f(-2))$. $f(x)$ means 'function of x'. The graph of a linear function of x is a straight line where $f(x) = 3x + 2$, for example. By substituting values for x the values of the function can be found. These values of the function are the second coordinates of points on the graph of the function.

A table of values and a graph of the function are shown below:

x	$f(x)$			
0	3×0	$+ 2 =$	2
1	3×1	$+ 2 =$	5
2	3×2	$+ 2 =$	8
-1	$3 \times (-1)$	$+ 2 =$	-1
-2	$3 \times (-2)$	$+ 2 =$	-4

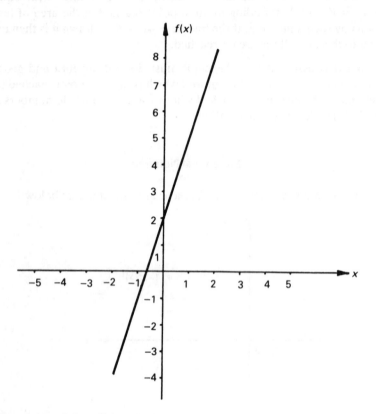

Another way of describing the line is $f : x \rightarrow 3x + 2$, i.e. 'f such that x is mapped on to $3x + 2$'.

Similarly $f(x) = ax^2 + bx + c$ or $f : x \rightarrow ax^2 + bx + c$ would be a quadratic function whose graph is a parabola.

Again, $f(x) = \sin x$ is a trigonometric function and $f(\pi) = \sin \pi$ for example.

ACCURATE DRAWINGS

Some investigations may require fairly accurate diagrams for which the following methods may be found useful. Drawings like these are called constructions.

A Dividing a line into two equal parts.

    1. Take the line, AB

2. With your compass set at a radius which is larger than half the length of the line

3. Put the point of the compass at one end of the line, A, and mark an arc above and below the line.

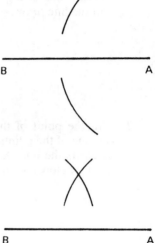

4. Keeping the same radius put the point of the compass on the other end of the line, B, and draw arcs to cut the previous ones above and below the line.

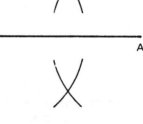

5. Join the points where the arcs cut each other.

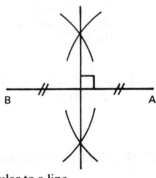

Notice that the method also gives a line which is at right angles to the first one.

B   Drawing a line from a point to be perpendicular to a line.

P •

1. Put the point of the compass on the point P and with a radius that is big enough to cut the line draw an arc.

2. Put the point of the compass on one of the points where the arc cuts the line, X, and draw an arc below the line.

3. Put the point of the compass on the other point, Y, where the arc cuts the line and draw an arc to cut the one below the line.

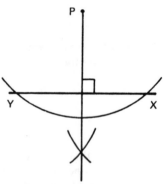

4. Join P to where the arcs cut each other.

C   Drawing a perpendicular to a line, AB, through a point, P, on the line.

1. Put the point of the compass on P and draw an arc on each side of P to cut the line at X and Y.

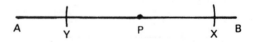

2. Put the point on the compass on the point X and draw an arc above the line.

3. Put the point of the compass on Y and with the same radius draw an arc to cut the first one.

4. Join P to the point where the arcs cut each other.

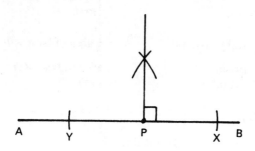

FORMULÆ

1. **Length.**

Perimeter of a square	$4l$
Perimeter of a rectangle	$2l + 2b$ or $2(l + b)$
Circumference of a circle	$2\pi r$
Length of an arc of a circle	$\dfrac{\theta}{360} \times 2\pi r$

Pythagoras: $a^2 = b^2 + c^2$, where a is the length of the hypotenuse.

2. **Area.**

Area of a square	l^2
Area of a rectangle	lb
Area of a triangle	$\frac{1}{2}bh$
Area of a circle	πr^2
Area of a sector of a circle	$\dfrac{\theta}{360} \times \pi r^2$
Surface area of a sphere	$4\pi r^2$
Surface area of a cone	$\pi r(s + r)$
Curved surface area of a cone	πrs
Curved surface area of a cylinder	$2\pi rh$

Total surface area of a closed cylinder = $2\pi r(h + r)$

3. **Volume.**

Volume of a cube	l^3
Volume of a cuboid	lbh
Volume of a sphere	$\frac{4}{3}\pi r^3$
Volume of a cone	$\frac{1}{3}\pi r^2 h$
Volume of a right pyramid	$\frac{1}{3}$ area of base $\times h$
Volume of a prism	area of base $\times h$
Volume of a cylinder	$\pi r^2 h$

4. **Trigonometry.**

$$\frac{a}{\sin \hat{A}} = \frac{b}{\sin \hat{B}} = \frac{c}{\sin \hat{C}} \quad \text{(Sine Rule)}$$

$$a^2 = b^2 + c^2 - 2bc \cos \hat{A}$$

$$\cos \hat{A} = \frac{b^2 + c^2 - a^2}{2bc} \qquad \text{Cosine Rule}$$

$$\frac{\sin x}{\cos x} = \tan x$$

$$\sin^2 x + \cos^2 x = 1$$

$$A = \tfrac{1}{2}ab \sin \hat{C} \quad \text{(Area of a triangle.)}$$

5. **Coordinates.**

$$d = \sqrt{(x_2 - x_1)^2 + (y_2 - y_1)^2} \qquad \text{(Distance formula)}$$

$$\left(\frac{x_1 + x_2}{2}, \frac{y_1 + y_2}{2}\right) \quad \text{(Mid point)}$$

$$m = \frac{y_2 - y_1}{x_2 - x_1} \qquad \text{(gradient, } m\text{)}$$

6. **Quadratic formula.**

$$x = \frac{-b \pm \sqrt{b^2 - 4(a)(c)}}{2a}$$

Printed by Bell and Bain Ltd., Glasgow